1   Brentford Dock at low tide, 1964
       Showing engine house, accumulator tower, Shunters' cabin,
       subsidence of 1961, scar from 40 ton crane, riverside crane and
       tracks, floodgate etc

BRENTFORD DOCK

AND

RAILWAY

DIANA WILLMENT

Dandelion Publications

By the author of :

Brentford Walk A, The River Thames and Old Brentford, 2001
Brentford Walk B, The Grand Junction Canal and New Brentford
Fire ! 300 Years of Fire Fighting in Brentford, 2002
Brentford's Public Inscriptions, 2002
Brentford Fountain Kew Bridge, 2003
Brentford Library and the First Librarian, 2004
The Boatmen's Institute Brentford, 2004
Sir Montagu Sharpe Forgotten Man of Middlesex, 2007

Published by:
Dandelion Publications (Brentford)
Brentford Dock

Second edition, September 2009
Reprinted, July 2012

I S B N : 978-0-9540590-5-7

Technical Processing:
adam.watson@stradivari.net

Printing :
Blissett Digital, Roslin Road, London, W3 8DN
www.blissetts.com

CONTENTS

ILLUSTRATIONS

"It is rather a dignified term to call it a Dock"

Isambard Kingdom Brunel
14th May 1855

BRENTFORD DOCK AND RAILWAY

Introduction

The great mystery at Brentford Dock in the late 20th century was entrenched local tradition that the Dock was built by Isambard Kingdom Brunel. The mystery lay in the absence of any mention of the Dock, even of Brentford, from biographies of Brunel. The massive rounded stone blocks edging the Dock near the entrance could well be Brunellian, but it was clear from popular accounts of his life that in the late 1850s, when the Dock was under construction, Brunel was far too preoccupied elsewhere to be involved in the undertaking himself. By 1859 he was a sick man, suffering from overwork and failing kidneys. He died on 15 September 1859, two months after the opening of the Dock. But although Brunel had little or nothing to do with the construction of the Dock, in the mid 1850s he undoubtedly did design both the railway link from the GWR at Southall to Brentford and the trans-shipment dock at the Thames. As Chief Engineer to the Great Western Railway (GWR) and Great Western & Brentford Railway (GW&BR) he also carried overall responsibility

National trade needed a reliable transport link from the railway network north and west of London to the import and export docks in east London. Brunel, speaking in the interests of the GWR and proposed GW&BR Companies, played an important part in convincing Parliament that there could be a better option than the Grand Junction Canal between the GWR and the Thames

Brentford Dock, initially called the Great Western Dock, was opened in July 1859. It closed to goods traffic at the end of 1964. Closure was caused by a reduction in traffic, the demise of the 40 ton crane, neglect and finally, Dr Richard Beeching

This account outlines the planning and construction of Brentford Dock and its Railway, their useful life over the next hundred years and eventual closure to goods traffic. It is an endeavour to bring together material related to the designing, building and operation of Dock and Railway in a local history context. Material has been gathered from Parliamentary Records, Brunel's deposited plans, archived documents, biographies of Brunel, railway histories and journals, *The Times*, local newspapers and other sources both published and unpublished. Technical details have been generously supplied by members of the Greater London Industrial Archaeology Society from evaluation in the field and archived sources. There is a first-hand account of working as a Shunter at the Dock in the early 1960s. Due credit is given to both Designer and Resident Engineer for their parts in an enterprise important for national prosperity

The building of Brentford Dock housing estate by the Greater London Council in the 1970s is not covered, nor the development of the Dock as a Marina in the early 1980s. That is another story, the telling of which is left for others

1

The Grand Junction Canal

In the 18th century canals represented a great improvement over roads for the transport of goods. Roads were difficult enough in summer and often impassable in winter. Canals were well suited for the movement of such heavy non-perishable cargoes as coal, timber, pottery, bricks, hay and refuse

The Grand Junction Canal, engineered by William Jessop and started in 1792, used the River Brent for its first 3 miles from the Thames at Brentford to Hanwell. By 1794 it was complete to Uxbridge via Bull's Bridge and reached Braunston in 1805. In 1820 the Paddington Arm from Bull's Bridge Junction was opened and the Regent's Canal reached Regent's Dock and the River Lea in 1855. The Slough Arm was opened in 1883. When first constructed Thames Lock and the Gauging Lock in Brentford were single locks, both have since been doubled

In the 19th century the canal system was overtaken by another advance in transport efficiency. From 1829 it was clear that a railway could move heavy goods in bulk at least ten times as fast as a canal. The railway network expanded rapidly

Lott's Mead, Town Meadow and Old England

What was there before the Dock was built ? Who were the owners and occupiers ?

The land between the Rivers Brent and Thames upon which the Dock was built is shown on a Parish Boundary map of 1777 as New-Brentford Town Mead and Lot Meadow (see illustration No 2). A lot meadow was formerly a common meadow, shared out by lot. The names 'mead' and 'meadow' suggest grazing and hay, and they are likely to have been largely water meadows. In the 18th and early 19th centuries the area was shown or described as at least partly osier beds and osiers (young willows) need moist ground. Maps drawn before the Grand Junction

2

Canal was built, show a marshy Brent delta with distributaries running to the Thames across Lot Meadow (Lott's Mead) and Town Meadow (Mead). The largest wriggled towards the Thames more or less due south of Workhouse Dock. Another smaller straighter one, partly a drainage ditch and labelled `Creek', ran south of Thames Locks (see Nos 3 and 4). This was roughly the route of the ancient boundary between Old and New Brentford. A parish boundary marker survives at Thames Locks. An OS map of 1897 shows the water meadows in Syon Park as Old England (see No 20)

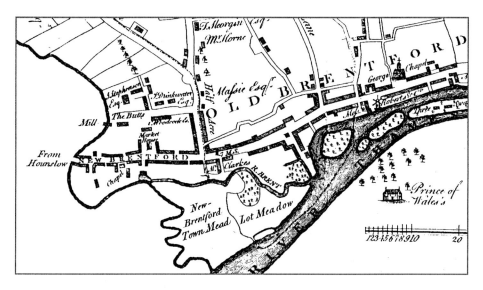

2   Ealing Parish Boundary Survey, 1777
       Showing New-Brentford Town Mead and Lot Meadow

It is possible that the canalisation of the lower Brent and stopping up of delta streams in the early 1790s caused the meadows to dry out and consolidate to some extent. However most of the water lying on this ground came from the tidal Thames. The land level around the Dock has been raised, although some of this was done later for the housing estate. The water meadows in Syon Park, where land levels are lower, are still frequently flooded by the Thames. Peter King reports friction between the Duke of Northumberland and the GWR and GW&BR Companies over who should fill in ditches on the Duke's land near the site where the Dock was to be built.. B Cook notes that there was a shortage of ballast for this soggy ground and substantial quantities of in-fill were obtained from excavations for the Metropolitan Railway which was under construction at the time (BC,1994). The GWR conveyed the material to Brentford and the job may have fallen to them

The Act of 1855 (see below) describes Town Meadow as `an osier bed'; Brunel names five owners for it. Around the town and further westward, was a market garden district important for feeding London, and there was an ancient market in Brentford. Much of the neighbouring riverside carried osier beds, which were a vital adjunct to the market garden industry and there are still productive osier beds on nearby Isleworth Ait. The osiers were used to make baskets for transporting fruit and vegetables to market. Some owners and occupiers of osier beds objected to losing this source of income to the proposed Dock

In his evidence to the Parliamentary Select Committee (see below), Brunel names John Clarke, Lady Delpierre, James Montgomrey, Lord Jersey and the Duke of Northumberland as land owners affected by the project. The first deposited plan names Lady Croft Delpierre, the Duke of Northumberland, James Montgomrey, Thomas Fisher and Philip Worsley. The Duke of Northumberland owned part of the land needed for the Dock. The Montgomreys owned a timber yard east of Dock Road, the land required for Dock Road and part of Town Meadow needed for the Dock. John Clarke owned property to the west of Dock Road. John Fuller of Chiswick brewers Fuller, Smith & Turner owned cottages and a parcel of land needed for the railway at the north end of Ham Common in Brentford. The Earl of Jersey owned most of the land required for the railway further north

The Book of Reference to Deposited Plans gives the names of owners and occupiers of fields at Three Bridges, Hanwell in 1854 :
1 Arable, owners Middlesex Justices of the Peace
2 Meadow, GJC Co, leased to J&R Trumper of Warren Farm
3 Arable and wharf, Earl of Jersey, leased to J&R Trumper

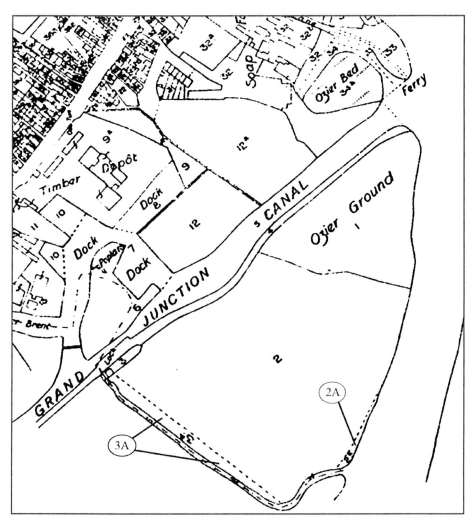

3

Ealing Tithe Map, 1839
1 Lot Meadow, John Clarke & Thomas Bowden;
2 Lot Meadow, John Clarke;   2a Duke of Northumberland;
3a Rectorial Glebe, John Clarke; 6,7 James Montgomrey;
10,11 Major John Sharp

On 29 January 1857 a meeting was convened by the GW&BR Co, and advertised in the press. It took place in the Vestry of St Lawrence's Church, New Brentford and was presided over by William Bolster Whitman. Present were 22 citizens of Brentford, a majority of those entitled to Commonable, Lammas or other rights over lands at Old England and Town Meadow. A Committee was elected to treat with the GW&BR Co for compensation to be paid for the extinction of these rights. The Committee consisted of James Racketts, John Coles, Henry Barnes, James Pearce and William Barnes (Vestry Minutes, 29 January 1857)

On 21 July 1870 *The Times* reports that a Bill to restrain the GW&BR from running their trains over part of Lott's Meadow near Brentford had been drafted. In 1856 Miss Fawell, a part owner, had been unable to establish the boundary of her property which was rented to Mr Clarke.

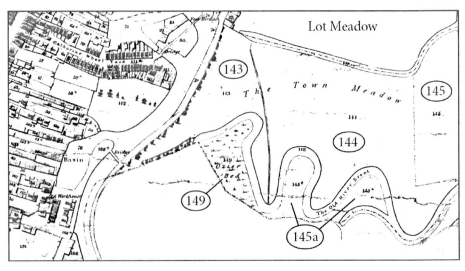

4   Township of New Brentford in the County of Middlesex, 1839
       143   James Montgomrey
       144   William & Henry Jupp
       145, 145a, Duke of Northumberland   145a Osiers
       149   Matthew Bowden

Miss Fawell was not paid purchase money or compensation and died before the matter was resolved. The compulsory purchase powers of the GW&BR Co expired in August 1859. The Company had continued in possession without taking enough trouble to compensate Miss Fawell or the new owner and a rope set up across the track had been broken through. The case was found against the plaintiff but the Railway Company had to pay costs

Isambard Kingdom Brunel

Who was Isambard Kingdom Brunel ? What was he doing in the late 1850s, if not building Brentford Dock ?

Marc Isambard Brunel, later Sir Marc, a native of Normandy, was a successful engineer and innovator. Having Royalist sympathies he left France at the time of the French Revolution. In 1799, after living briefly in New York State, Marc settled in London and married Sophia Kingdom. Their third child and only son was born in 1806 in Portsmouth, he was named Isambard Kingdom. The young Brunel was educated and briefly apprenticed in northern France. Aged 19 he returned to England to work as apprentice to his father, helping him with his projects. In 1833, at the age of 27, young Brunel was appointed Engineer by the Bristol Railway Company. This became the Great Western Railway Company when King William IV gave his assent to the Great Western Railway Bill in 1835. Brunel continued to have overall responsibility for engineering on the GWR for the rest of his life and under him the GWR developed as a broad gauge railway. He married Mary Horsley in 1836

From 1853 to 1857 Brunel was designing and overseeing the construction of the Saltash railway bridge between Devon and Cornwall. In 1854/5 he was experimenting with floating gun carriages, and designing guns and a hospital for the troops in the Crimea. He was also busy travelling between London and the house being built for him in the West Country. From 1855 to 1857 Brunel was preoccupied with designing and redesigning the iron ship, the Great Eastern, by far the largest ship ever built at the time.

It was being built at the shipyard of John Scott Russell on the Isle of Dogs in east London, with Brunel as Engineer. He chose 3 November 1857 as the launch date. The first launch attempt failed and, assisted by his second son Henry, Brunel finally forced the great ship into the Thames in the chill of January 1858

Brunel's health had been failing for some time. Doctors ordered a trip to Europe in May 1858 and to Egypt later that year to avoid the British winter. The party, including his wife and son, left for Egypt in mid-December 1858, returning to London in early May 1859. Brunel missed Prince Albert's formal opening of the Saltash Bridge by a few days. By this time the fitting out of the Great Eastern was well advanced and the main work was completed by 25th July 1859

Brunel was not well enough to attend the banquet given by Russell on board the Great Eastern on 5th August. The maiden voyage was to be to Weymouth and Holyhead on 3rd September and there was a flurry of activity as last minute jobs were hurriedly completed. On 2nd September 1859 final engine trials were carried out and Brunel posed on the ship for photographs. He collapsed from a heart attack immediately after. He suffered paralysis and was carried home to Duke Street in London. The voyage was delayed until 7th September when the ship was towed out to Purfleet by tugs. On 8th September the anchor was ceremoniously raised and the SS Great Eastern steamed down the Thames estuary and into the English Channel

Off Dungeness there was an explosion from inside the ship. Several stokers were badly injured by scalding water and steam, and five of them died. The ship had been fitted with annular water tanks round the funnels to pre-heat the feed-water to the boilers, one of Brunel's innovations. The annular tank at the forward funnel had exploded, said at the inquest to have been caused by the closure of a vital valve on a vent, and possibly a deliberate act. The ship was not seriously disabled and carried on to Weymouth. News of the disaster was conveyed to Brunel despite suggestions that it should be delayed to let him recover a little

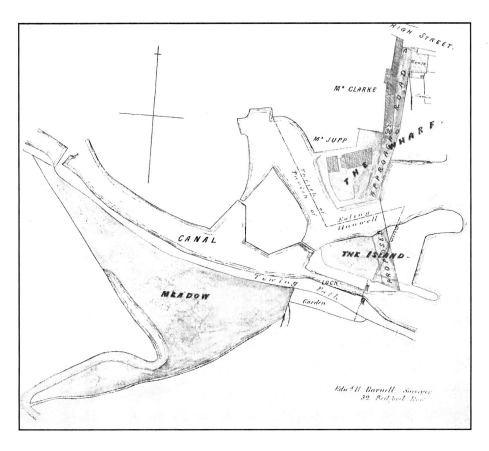

5   Agreement between James 'Montgomery' and the GW&BR Company, 26th November 1855. Montgomrey owned the shaded parts. The purchase price was £3,775 but Montgomrey had to accept £2,000 in Company shares in part payment (see agreement with contractor Thomas Treadwell, below)

Difficulties and disagreements over the SS Great Eastern and the catastrophe off Dungeness played their parts in sapping Brunel's remaining strength. He died on Thursday 15th September 1859. He was 53

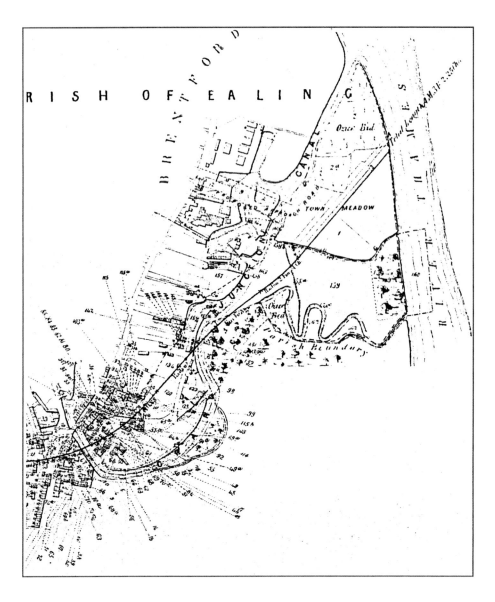

6   First deposited plan 1854, drafted by W D Haskoll. Shows the railway in Brentford and the Dock at an early stage of planning

Willam Davis Haskoll and Edward Francis Murray

If not Brunel then who ?

Although separate companies, the Great Western Railway and Great Western & Brentford Railway Companies were closely linked from the start. Some directors of the new company were already directors or shareholders of the GWR. Brunel was appointed Engineer, later designated Engineer-in-Chief, to the GW&BR. He continued to carry overall responsibility for engineering to both Companies until his death. W. Davis Haskoll was appointed Assistant Acting Engineer, later Acting Engineer, by the GWR Company under Brunel. Haskoll claimed to be a Resident Engineer on the Smyrna and Aidin Railway and the Great Western & Brentford Railway & Dock, etc. He was probably Resident Engineer to the proposed GW&BR for well under a year until the appointment of Murray some time before 15 May 1855. Construction on the project did not actually start for nearly another year, after 3 March 1856. Haskoll wrote a number of works on surveying, tunnelling and the practical details of railway construction. He was the author of *Railway Construction*, published 1864, in which he includes an impressive scale plan of Brentford Dock carrying the names 'Brunell' and Haskoll (see No 13)

Edward Murray was born in Belfast in May 1818 and studied architecture and drawing in France and Italy. He became an assistant to Brunel and helped him with some of his projects including Box Tunnel on the GWR. He travelled with Brunel to northern Italy where he helped lay out a railway between Genoa and Alessandria and assisted on other Italian railway projects. Murray was Assistant Engineer on Brunel's West Cornwall Railway and Resident Engineer on GWR branch lines to Windsor, Henley and Uxbridge. Murray was appointed Assistant Engineer, later Resident Engineer, to the GW&BR under Brunel (BDCE,2008). He was made Engineer-in-Chief to the GW&BR after the death of Brunel

The names of Brunel and Haskoll are on the first deposited plans for the Brentford Railway and Dock, dated 30 November 1854 (see Nos 6 and

11

10). Murray's name is on the second deposited plan for a proposed footbridge over the River, which also shows the Dock as actually built. This plan is dated 30th November 1860 (see No 7). The two sets of plans were probably drafted by or under Haskoll and Murray respectively, to the designs of the busy Brunel. As Resident Engineer to the GW&BR, Murray oversaw the day-to-day work of construction of the Brentford Railway and Dock. Murray later built road bridges over the Thames at Walton, Pangbourne and Hampton Court

Murray built the Dock railway as shown on the first deposited plan of 1854, and described by Brunel in his evidence to the Parliamentary Select Committee (see Nos 6 and 10). He built the Dock to the second deposited plan (see No 7)

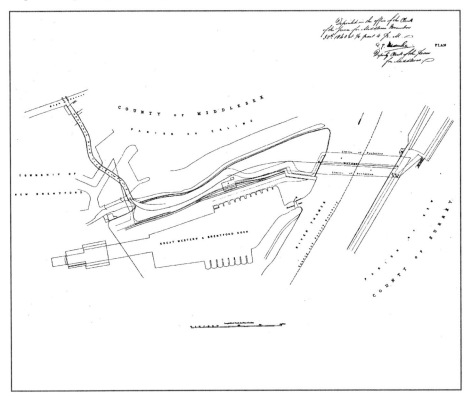

7   Second deposited plan 1860, drafted by E F Murray.
     Shows the Dock and proposed footbridge across the Thames

Apparently it was Murray who had the idea of extending Dock Road to a point north of the Dock entrance. He proposed a footbridge over the river giving access to Kew Gardens. He would purchase the Brentford ferry and levy tolls on the footbridge

The Grand Junction Canal is Inadequate

The problem the GWR Co was trying to solve was that the narrow congested streets of London lay between its terminus at Paddington and the import and export docks at the Pool of London. London was a serious bottleneck for trade between the industrial areas of England and South Wales, and suppliers and customers on the continent. The practical choice for goods travelling by GWR was to cart over poor roads from Southall or Hayes to the river at Brentford, or to transfer to canal boats at the GWR depot at Hayes and use the GJC to Brentford. The GWR depot was just north-east of Hayes station (now called Hayes and Harlington) and known by the local name, Bull's Bridge. In the depot was a basin connected to the GJC for transfer of goods between rail and canal (see No 8). At Brentford goods were transferred to Thames barges or lighters and then transferred again to sea-going vessels at the London Docks

Unfortunately the Canal was too narrow, too slow and too expensive. The charge for shipping by Canal from Bull's Bridge to Brentford was the same as to London anywhere above Woolwich. The Canal could suffer from water shortages in dry summers and freeze-ups in cold winters. Small heavily laden horse-drawn narrow-boats were not suitable for the onward journey down the Thames to the Pool of London. Thames barges could not easily pass each other in the Canal. One submerged boat could delay traffic for days. Before 1835/6 the Canal was closed at night to heavy traffic to allow lighter craft through

The GWR was broad gauge and the only other option for London goods was to transfer to railways belonging to other Companies. This would have meant a change of gauge and charges which could be heavy. Every

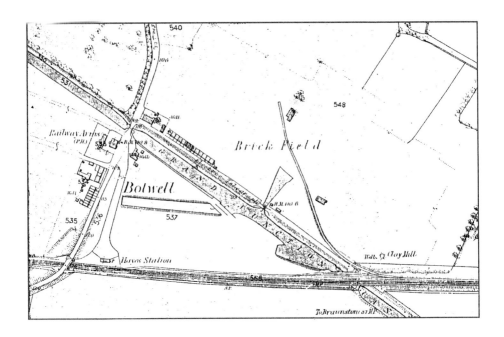

8   Hayes Station and Bull's Bridge GWR Depot.
Canal basin under the word 'Botwell'. The Bull's Bridge
GJC Canal Depot is about ¾ mile SW of GWR Depot at the junction
with the Paddington Arm. Ordnance Survey, 1865. Crown Copyright

transfer of goods was expensive, it took manpower, horsepower and time and cargoes risked deterioration. By the mid 19th century industry was growing rapidly and the country relied increasingly on imports and exports; as a busy manufacturing town, Brentford generated trade of its own

The Times, 16 July 1859 : "Hitherto, all the heavy traffic on the Great Western Railway destined for the Port of London has left the main line at Bull's-bridge, whence it has been taken down the Grand Junction Canal to Brentford. For a long time past the means of transport thus afforded has proved quite inadequate for the greatly increased traffic which the opening up of the Welsh coalfields and the connexion of the Great Western line with Birmingham, Wolverhampton, Birkenhead, Liverpool and other places have brought upon it. Between Bull's-bridge and Brentford there are upon the canal no fewer than 11 locks, and the delay which these occasioned was enhanced in winter by frosts and in summer by droughts. The tonnage dues also were heavy, and all these circumstances affected very prejudicially the goods and mineral traffic upon the trunk line."

The plan was to link the railway network to the River Thames, bypassing the GJC. The GWR Co wanted an outlet to the Thames over broad gauge track of their own and their own trans-shipment dock to transfer goods between rail and river. Building a rail link from Southall on the GWR to Brentford on the Thames less than 5 miles away and a dock for transferring goods to Thames barges would eliminate one transfer. Raw materials and finished goods would move more speedily and cheaply between the country's industrial heartlands and the Pool of London. Coal was a principal cargo and circumventing London's congestion by using the river improved reliability - and avoided London coal dues

Articles from *The Times*

The Times newspaper published reports of the half-yearly Board meetings of the Great Western & Brentford Railway Company. It is reasonable to use *The Times*, the national newspaper of record at the time, for reports of Company meetings

The subsidiary company was set up and the first formal meeting of the directors of the new Great Western & Brentford (Thames Junction) Railway Company was on 24 August 1854. They discussed the making of a railway from Southall to Brentford. The Earl of Jersey who owned Osterley Park and much of the land required for the railway, was more amenable than the Duke of Northumberland who owned part of the land needed for the Dock, and whose house at Syon was closer to the proposed railway. The Duke eventually acquiesced, "sacrificing his private feelings to the advantage of the neighbourhood". There was a list of officials and organisations who would have to be informed and give their consent. The GWR Co offered support (non-financial); they would lease the facilities when complete and use their own rolling stock

9   Southall Station in 1852

28 November 1854 : The second meeting considered a proposal to "construct a railway from the Great Western Railway at Southall to Brentford near to the bank of the river Thames.
It is also proposed to construct docks, wharves, quays and tramways at Brentford, and to obtain powers in the ensuing session [of Parliament] for running over the Great Western line, and for authorising the latter company to run its engines and carriages over the proposed line to Brentford upon such terms and conditions as may be mutually agreed upon."

The proposals were carried

Evidence to the Parliamentary Select Committee

Mr Mellor (cross-examining) : " this ditch of a canal"
Mr Beck (wharfinger, Isleworth) : "this detestable ditch"

An Act of Parliament is needed for a major undertaking involving compulsory purchase of property. Before a Bill for such a scheme can become an Act, a Select Committee examines the proposal carefully, taking evidence both for and against. In May 1855 evidence was given to the House of Commons Select Committee on Railway Bills. The subject was the proposed Great Western & Brentford (Thames Junction) Railway. Written petitions against the Bill had been submitted by the London & South Western Railway Company (L&SWR), by Sophia Jane Lateward Delpierre and the Duke of Northumberland. These objectors did not attend the hearing. There was also opposition from the Great Northern Railway and the Grand Junction Canal Companies

The Parliamentary record shows that evidence in favour of the Bill was given on 11 May 1855 by officials and tradesmen, local and non-local. Counsel for the Bill were Mr Merewether and Mr Hardy, with Mr H E Adair in the Chair. The following points were made :

Frederick Whitehouse and William Farnell (brewers, Brentford and Isleworth) : Both wanted easier access to the Uxbridge barley market and Thames Valley grain markets via Southall and delays at Bull's-bridge injured their malt. Half of Mr Farnell's malt came by the GWR and road. There were steep road bridges over the GWR and over the Canal at Norwood where extra horses were needed. Isleworth and its huge cornmill would benefit from the railway. Salt was difficult to obtain. Coal was needed by brewers, soapmakers and the waterworks, all coal users wanted better cheaper coal. Welsh steam coal was 10% better than any other, but delivery to Brentford cost as much as to London. Coal coming from elsewhere by sea and up the Thames was smokey and cartage expensive. Delays on the Canal from Bull's-bridge when the Canal was frozen caused coal to run out because of limited space in brewery coal stores. A dock at Brentford would save at least two shillings per ton on transport. A barge could get from Brentford to London Docks on one tide, considerably less using steam tugs. This would cost one shilling to one shilling and threepence per ton. Cartage from Paddington cost at least five shillings per ton. Other routes via Brentford Station [using a route through Willesden Junction and Kew Bridge], Kensington, 'Punch's' line [the line from nowhere to nowhere] etc were slow and expensive, and more transfers were needed. [These lines did not belong to the GWR and were not broad gauge.] The proposed scheme would develop the coal and mineral trade and Brentford residents were in favour because as a coaching town Brentford had suffered loss of trade because of railway development. It was possible that the town would benefit from visitors to Kew Gardens who might come this way and use the ferry; the ferry cost a ha'penny

Edward Beck (general merchant and wharfinger, Isleworth) : Isleworth with its large wharf (the best equipped in London) imported stone for churches and for building at Kew and Hampton Court. With the new railway and dock Mr Beck would get his stone in 48 hours. He preferred to get Bath, Portland and York stone from Brentford rather than by sea. He says that there was only one crane at Bull's-bridge

James Tapping (master lighterman, 30 years at Brentford) : says that because of lack of water, narrow-boats could not carry their full loads. An 80 ton boat carried 45 to 72 tons at most. Overtaking was not possible and slow-moving barges could cause fights to break out. Delays were also caused by annual stoppages to repair locks, rope breakages when boats got stuck in locks (sometimes actually suspended in mid-air at Horsley Lock, Osterley), and larger boats unable to pass each other sometimes had to wait 5-6 hours to let one get down. From Bull's-bridge to Brentford should take 4 hours but could take all day and all night. The traffic was clearly too heavy for the GJC

Peter Davey (coal trade) : A coal depot was needed at Brentford as property was too expensive for merchants to keep their own large coal depots and coal deteriorates if much broken. The Gas Company and "three stupendous engines" for water pumping at Hampton would need Welsh coal. He says that steam vessels were getting larger, Westminster Bridge was being rebuilt, and locks were about to be built at Teddington and further upstream to improve water depths in the Thames

Bernard Gilpin (edgetool & iron manufacturer, S Staffordshire) : Needed rapid transport for his heavy iron goods so that they could be loaded first into the bottoms of ships; delays at Bull's-bridge upset his arrangements. He did not get much notice of shipping dates, his products needed to get to the London Docks within three days

William Marr (Agent, Aberdare & Ebbw Vale Works, S Wales) : He sent 46,000 tons of steam coal last year to manufactories on the Thames and the demand was increasing. From Bull's-bridge to Brentford was inefficient on the Canal

The hearing was adjourned and continued on 14 May 1855

James Forbes (Goods Traffic Manager to GWR at Paddington) : A lot of money had been laid out to improve Bull's-bridge Depot in 1852 and 1853, because of the extension of lines to Wales and the North. There were 2,000 feet of wharfage. Traffic was uneven, most of it was for London and the Docks. There had been an enormous increase of traffic in grain, coal, iron, copper and tin. Copper from Swansea, raw sugar from Millwall Docks to Bristol for refining, timber to Woolwich for shipbuilding all used the River rather than the Regent's Canal. Rail was better than canal under any circumstances and traffic could only increase. When there were problems with frost Paddington had to be used, although frost could affect the River too. Goods from Staffordshire went to Willesden, Kew and Waterloo and they were considering using Battersea; it was better to take goods to the riverside, but it was easier to load and unload at a non-tidal canal. Goods were often urgent, Bull's-bridge could only cope with the non-urgent

John Bishop (Superintendent of Goods at Bull's-bridge) : Lowness of water reduced loads by 5-10 tons and that meant more horses were needed. The Thames was affected by frost one week less at the beginning and end of a freeze-up. Barges worked on the Thames a week after the canal was closed, and a week before it reopened. Barges could get left behind at Brentford as there was only one lock, these had to wait for the next tide. The previous summer the Canal was totally blocked by one brick barge

Charles Sherriff (Manager of Messrs Kidds & Podger, flour mill at Isleworth, largest in England) : Wishes to obtain wheat from western markets via Reading and Newbury. It now comes from Cambridgeshire and Lincolnshire via Blackwall Station London

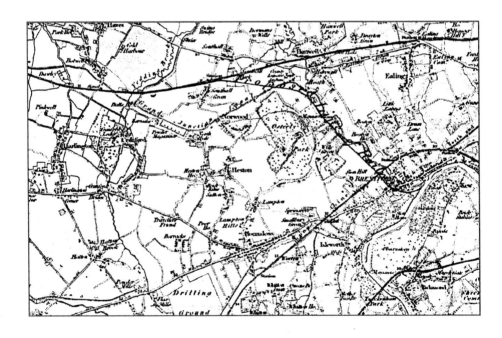

10   First deposited plan 1854, drafted by W D Haskoll.
        Shows proposed railway route between Southall and Brentford

Mr. Brunel Answers Some Questions

The Parliamentary record for 14 May 1855 shows the hearing continuing with evidence from Brunel

Mr 'Isambert' K Brunel (Engineer to this Company and the Great Western Railway) :

Mr Brunel maintains that the Great Western & Brentford (Thames Junction) Railway Company is an independent company. He says that Bull's-bridge can handle as much traffic as the canal can carry away. There is enough trade for two channels of communication between Bull's-bridge and Brentford. He describes a proposed rail route from Southall station descending to the river at Brentford

The line passed by the north-east side of Osterley Park, near the Grand Junction Canal and Hanwell Lunatic Asylum [Middlesex County Asylum], under the Canal, over the South Western Railway near Brentford, and over the turnpike by a bridge whose dimensions had been arranged with the Metropolitan Land Commissioners "without affecting those works". It then crossed over the canal twice, in one case very obliquely, before entering the ground where it was proposed to carry the line to the River. The bridges would give more headway than the "heavy stone bridge [taking] the road over the canal". The railway would be high enough not to need an incline; the bridges would be higher than usual. "After the last crossing we enter the Town Meadow which adjoins the River and for the purpose of shipping into the barges we might make a cut into the River". The estimated cost is £90,000. "What depth of water do you propose to have in the new Dock ?" "I propose at present about twelve feet from ordinary spring tides". It is pointed out that the Canal proprietors are concerned about the track passing under their Canal at Hanwell. Brunel says he has made six crossings of railways under canals and there were plenty of others. Sixteen feet were needed for engines and twenty feet were available, he would use a cast iron trough for the Canal. He plans to acquire land for a double line and some sidings, but most of it would actually be single track

Q : What proportion do you attribute to the new Docks ?
A : £10,000. It is rather a dignified term to call it a Dock. It would be a slip into the River
Q : You have expended four times that amount at Bull's-bridge?
A : Not on the docks

[From August 1853 new dock and canal wharfage, buildings, sidings and hydraulic equipment were built and installed by the GWR at Bull's Bridge Depot. Opened 1856 (TS)]

Q : What quantity of land do you propose to occupy at Brentford ?
A : About 6 acres - not by docks
Q : By Docks and wharves, warehouses and so on ?
A : I do not suppose there would be warehouses. I can hardly tell you. If we have to make a timberyard we should occupy a good deal of land
Q : What in your £10,000 do you contemplate to do ?
A : Merely to carry the Railway alongside a dock or slip ... and buying land sufficient to spread out timber or other things ... if necessary
Q : How much land do you propose to take in Town Meadow ?
A : I think 6 acres
Q : What is the land as distinct from the works - the line ?
A : £19,000 I think
Q : Do you propose to construct a lock at Brentford ?
A : A lockgate to the slip
Q : Is it to be a single lockgate ?
A : I have really hardly made up my mind
Q : ... is the dock to be tidal ?
A : ... not decided
Q : Do you propose to build a station here ?
A : No ... If we ever put in a passenger station it would be here
Points to location on plan
Q : ... what sort of water accommodation ... ?
A : Simply a cut with a Dock gate
Q : What width of water ... ?

A : About 80 feet then that cut is to extend up to the level part of that line

Q : That is for 15 chains it is to extend at a level ?

A : part of it only is for the entrance. The Dock itself would be 11 chains

The estimate is £76,318 for the railway plus £10,000 for the Dock. The approach road to the Dock is £2,800, surplus £1,200, said to total £90,000

Q : What sort of access have you from this Dock to the town ?

A : We include in the Act the power to make a small road to the Dock

Q : Is it from a portion of the town that is easily approached or is it out of a back street ?

A : It is the best access that could be made if you made it without the slightest regard to property or anything else ... we were able to arrange with an owner and ... laid it down exactly where we would wish [James Montgomrey, Dock Road]

Q : You seek ... to acquire under [the Act] 30 acres more ...

A : I did not know it was 30

Q : Do you contemplate the possibility of a very large extension of works on the banks of the River ?

A : That 30 acres I presumed is merely a form in Bills. If you think 30 too much make it 20

Q : These terms should be regulated according to the nature of the undertaking

A : They are filled in for the promoters. I do not contemplate, nor do they any such extension, and ... it can be diminished to any reasonable amount

Q : Where are your stations to be on this line ?

A : I do not imagine there will be any

Q : Will you not have a passenger station at Brentford ?

A : I do not know ...

Q : You take power to carry passengers

A : Yes. If we do carry passengers I imagine the station will be just north of the Turnpike road at Brentford

Q : On the incline of 1 in 128 ?

A : Just at the foot [?] of that, but the carrying of passengers is quite a secondary consideration

Q : Your bridge will be constructed for a double line ?

A : Our usual practice is to build bridges carrying a road over the railway for a double line because one cannot conveniently alter them but for a road under the railway single, because they can be made double

Q : Suppose in the case of this Canal bridge, if you had a subsequent necessity to widen the bridge at Hanwell would you disturb the works of the Canal ?

A : Where a bridge is carried over our railway that would be made double

Q : What is your normal gradient ?

A : 1 in 92

Q : Your worst curve ?

A : 16 chains

Q : Are there any particular engineering difficulties on the line ?

A : No

Q : Do you intend to have a separate station at ... Southall ?

A : I do not imagine we shall unless we carry passengers. There would be covered sidings as at Bull's-bridge ... 8 or 10 wagons would come down to Brentford and they would require sidings but there would be no station. The marshalling would be done at Southall ... the promoters ... would eventually have passengers ... Mr Meredith opened the case about the halfpenny fare to Kew Gardens. If there is a line going to a populous neighbourhood the inhabitants will want it

Charles Rogers (Secretary to Grand Junction Canal Company), gave evidence on behalf of the GJC Co :

He says that most cargoes are over 60 tons

Q : Can the ordinary canal barges used on the Thames pass at all times with great ease up and down your Canal ?

24

11   Middlesex County Asylum, near Hanwell, 1852.
Artist's interpretation from Uxbridge Road

A : Oh yes, with the greatest ease [!]. They can take water from the
Regent's [Canal] when the water drops enough ... below
the Parliamentary height ... The horse is not used ... [for a]
barge ascending or descending a lock, but immediately it gets
on a level, the horse-power is used
Q : Would there be any difficulty in doubling the lock so as to
accommodate any amount of traffic ?
A : None whatsoever ... it has been contemplated making an
additional lock at the Thames

Thames Lock was not doubled until 1960/61. Mr Rogers claims that the
Canal is able to pass two million tons per annum

Hearing adjourned until 15 May 1855 :

The Committee announced their decision that the Preamble to the Bill
was proved without alterations or additions

William Haskoll (Assistant Acting Engineer to GWR under Mr Brunel) answers :

Q : [The railway] is proposed to be constructed on a gauge of
    7 feet 4 inches ? [external measurement for broad gauge]
A : Yes

It might have been asked why money was being invested at Bull's Bridge if, before the 1853 improvements were complete, it was necessary to make another connection between the GWR and Brentford. The evidence to the Select Committee indicated that the traffic on the lower GJC had already reached capacity and the improvements at Bull's Bridge could only increase congestion. The proposed new scheme would make Bull's Bridge GWR Depot redundant. Congestion would be eased on the lower GJC as London goods would be transferred to and from the railway at Brentford

The GWR was completed from Paddington to Bristol in 1841. The transfer at Hayes of London goods via Brentford could not usefully have started much before this date. The new facilities at Bull's Bridge were opened in 1856 and the hydraulic equipment was relocated to Brentford Dock in 1859. Thus Bull's Bridge was used for transfer of London goods between Brentford and the GWR for less than 20 years, possibly much less in any quantity. The hydraulic plant operated at Bull's Bridge for about 3 years

It was reported in *The Times* on 2 June 1855, just prior to the passing of the 1855 Act, that the inhabitants of Brentford were invited by the GW&BR Co Directors to a meeting to "consider the propriety of supporting the above undertaking, Mr J 'Montgomery' in the chair. Mr H G Day, one of the Directors, having explained the advantages of the proposed line and docks to the town of Brentford and to the Great Western Railway Company, resolutions were passed in favour of the project". One of the consequences of the rosy picture painted by the Directors was a rush of applications for pub sites in the vicinity (RKK,2/1960,77)

26

The Act of 14 August 1855

To ensure that a major undertaking can be completed satisfactorily an Act allows a Company some leeway to purchase extra land and make deviations, but only within strict limits. Any excursions beyond those permitted in the Act and shown on deposited plans, would attract punitive penalties. Plans had to be deposited with a Justice of the Peace for the County (Middlesex) and signed by him. They carried the force of law

From the Parliamentary Record, 14 August 1855 :

"An Act for making a Railway from the Great Western Railway at Southall in the County of Middlesex to Brentford in the same County, with Docks at the last-mentioned place; and for other purposes." From Southall Station to Town Meadow, an osier bed in the Parish of Ealing ... [the parish of Old Brentford was still part of the parish of Ealing]. The gauge is to be 7 feet [internal measurement for broad gauge]. It would not be lawful for the Company to deviate southwards on to the Duke of Northumberland's property. Headroom at bridges is to be 16 feet. The turnpike is not to be more than half stopped off and the bridge finished in six months. At Hanwell the rails must be 26 feet below the Canal water surface. The Canal diversion must be restored within twelve months

"The proposed Dock or Docks ... [are to be] bounded on the South by the River Thames, on the North by the Grand Junction Canal, and on the West by Lands of His Grace the Duke of Northumberland. Previously to commencing the Dock entrance from the River Thames, or the works connected therewith, the Company shall deposit at the Admiralty Office Plans, Sections and working Drawings of the said Dock Entrance ... for the approval of the Lord High Admiral. The Dock must not be altered from deposited plans. The Railway and Docks shall be completed within four years ... a bond, three fortieths of £90,000, secures this." [£6,750] Clauses protected the Hounslow Loop of the London & South Western Railway and the Grand Junction Canal. The Act concluded with lists of maximum tolls for goods and the baggage allowances for passengers

The Act received the Royal Assent from Queen Victoria on 14 August 1855, and the Great Western & Brentford Railway Company was incorporated from this date. Various subsidiary Acts were approved to raise capital as needed to build the line and Dock by offering shares. The company was empowered within limits to purchase more land as needed, for a depot for Welsh smokeless coal for instance

More articles from *The Times*

5 March 1856 : The money was to be raised by issuing shares in stages and "share after share had been rapidly taken up ... by those ... who saw the importance of such an outlet to the Thames ... The directors had no hesitation in concluding contracts for the speedy execution of the works which were within the Parliamentary estimate". Mr Davey : " ... increasing the traffic of the Great Western Railway must shortly become so important that it would be impossible to carry it on without an outlet to the Thames. It was universally admitted by engineers that the cheapest and most advantageous mode of carrying goods was that which was afforded by a tidal stream."

29 Aug 1856 : " ... the directors had lost no time in making the necessary arrangements for commencing the works at once; and contractors of the greatest respectability had undertaken to execute the works ... possession of a great portion of the land had been obtained ... the contractors were actively engaged in the construction of the line and docks ... The Thames Steam-tug Company, lately formed, would afford the required facilities for discharging that traffic on the river". Mr Brunel, the engineer, stated in his report that "the works had been earnestly commenced, and that advantage had been taken of the late stoppage of the Grand Junction Canal to make provision for the contractor proceeding with the works without interfering with the navigation. Possession of the land had been obtained and several thousand yards from the principal cutting had been excavated and carried to embankment. Ground had been taken possession of near the river and the dock work had been commenced a few days since."

This is the last mention of Brunel in *The Times* in connection with the project, although the *West London Observer* mentions "Mr Brunel's unrivalled ingenuity" in the article of 23 July 1859. Brunel's reference in his report to taking advantage of a stoppage on the GJC may have been for the construction at Hanwell or for bridge construction at Brentford, possibly both. At Hanwell Brunel planned a temporary diversion of the Canal so that an iron trough to carry the Canal across the railway could be put in place. There was every incentive to complete the Hanwell crossing without hold-ups as there would be a penalty of £10 for every hour that boats were unable to pass. The only unco-operative occupiers of land on the whole project were the Trumpers of Warren Farm (RKK,1960,78). They occupied land needed for the temporary canal diversion at Three Bridges while the trough was being introduced

The contractor of the greatest respectability was Thomas Tredwell (Treadwell). He came of an established and prosperous family of contractors and civil engineers. Tredwell would be financially involved in the Brentford scheme, if awarded the assignment he would sign a subscription contract. He would be paid £30,000 and meanwhile take £15,000 stock in the Company, not to be sold until the line was open. If not awarded the contract he would receive £3,000 (BDCE,2008). Tredwell was successful and his company was authorised to start construction on 3 March 1856

23 February 1857 : It was reported in *The Times* at the GW&BR Co half-yearly meeting that progress was "rapid and satisfactory"

22 August 1857 : It was reported that a Bill passed through Parliament for an increase of capital to 45,000 l. The scheme was particularly needed for coals, for South Wales, the Mersey and Thames to be connected by an uninterrupted railway. " ... no project is more likely to restore the fallen fortunes of the Great Western Railway than this line."

27 February 1858 : - considerable progress - laying the permanent way - raising the remainder of capital authorised by Parliament - docks finished - bridges constructed - embankments ready for rails and machinery - one

12   Three Bridges, Hanwell, artist's interpretation by Ernest Ham.
Early 20th century

of the most valuable railway properties in the kingdom. Goods from Southall to Blackwall would be 4 to 5 shillings the ton instead of [7.5] to 10 shillings as now. The facility could be in use in two months

28 August 1858 : The works are in a very advanced state ... the contract for laying the permanent way is in course of execution. The dock is so far complete as to allow of the water being admitted so soon as the gates are erected... . It should be mentioned that a movement has taken place in part of the dock wall, and in one of the wing walls of the aqueduct bridge, these ... are now being restored

The only aqueduct in the project was at Hanwell. A movement at this significant spot must have been a severe blow to Murray. There was no further mention of any movement but see below 'The 40 ton Crane'

2 March 1859 : The Railway and Dock should be ready for traffic by the first week in May. "After a long negotiation with the Directors of the Great Western Railway Company an agreement for a lease of the railway, dock and accommodation works for a term of 99 years ... tolls on the transit of all goods and minerals ... sum of 500 l per annum would be derived from passenger traffic alone ... the dividend was expected to be more than 5%."

Evidence of Completion

The House of Commons Select Committee on Railway Bills, the Great Western & Brentford Railway to be leased to the Great Western Railway by this Bill, 3 March 1859. Evidence of completion was required before the Bill to lease the Railway and Dock to the GWR could become an Act

Mr Charles Eley, Secretary to the GW&BR Co, answers :

Q : Do you produce a copy of the ... Act of 1855 also of the ... Amendment Act of 1857 ?
A : Yes

Edward Francis Murray (Resident Engineer on the GW&B Railway) answers :

Q : The works have been constructed under your superintendence?
A : Yes ... The whole of the earth-work and bridges have been completed ... The permanent way is laid from the junction with the Great Western at Southall down to the Dock and the Dock has been finished ... with the exception of the covered sheds which are now constructing to accommodate the traffic of the GWR
Q : Is that a working drawing that you hold ?
A : This is a sketch of the Dock and I have also an ordnance map of the railway

31

House of Commons Select Committee on the GW&BR, 7 March 1859 : "The preamble of the Bill was again read and agreed to."

The Times, 1 March 1860 : The approach road to the dock from the town of Brentford was completed early in September [1859]. The GWR Company having already prepared station accommodation for passengers [Brentford Town], it was intended to open it in the spring. Notwithstanding the disadvantages attending the use of hand-power in the trans-shipment of goods during the removal of the hydraulic machinery from Bull's-bridge, the traffic conveyed up to the end of December [1859] had even then reached the monthly proportion of the guaranteed tonnage

Some Costs and Finances

The Times, Saturday 16th July 1859 :

"The Great Western Company undertake the working of the line, and guarantee to carry at least 100,000 tons of goods and minerals over it annually, exclusive of coal, coke, and stone. The present traffic at Bull's-bridge, however, and contracts already entered into, warrant the expectation that double the specified amount of traffic will pass over the line. It appears that the actual cost of these works, as executed by Messrs Treadwell, the contractors, under the super-intendance of Mr. E. F. Murray, the resident-engineer has been only 130,000 l; and the total cost from first to last, including preliminary law and Parliamentary expenses, and the purchase of land, has not exceeded 200,000 l."

The Act was passed on 14 August 1855 and the undertaking was started on 3 March 1856. It was opened in July 1859, so within the 4 years allotted by the Act. The total cost was over £200,000. Brunel's original estimate of £90,000 was for the works only and did not include land purchase, Parliamentary, legal and other costs. But it fell short of Murray's £130,000, Brunel certainly underestimated the cost

Both the GWR Co and the GW&BR Co had their financial difficulties in the late 1850s. *The Times* reports "fallen fortunes" of the GWR Co on 22 August 1857 (see above) and this increased their anxiety to sign a lease with the GW&BR Co. The "local company", the GW&BR Co, was reported to have run into financial difficulties when the project was almost complete in 1859 and to have turned to the GWR for help. The 99 year lease of the line and Dock was signed on 2 March 1859. The Great Western Railway Company took total possession on 15 September 1859, the last part to be completed being the road access, Dock Road

The Opening Ceremony, Friday 15th July 1859

Brentford has a proud tradition of marking important local occasions with lively public celebrations. There was the opening of the Grand Junction Canal in 1794, laying the foundation stone for the rebuilding of Brentford Bridge in 1824, the progress of Queen Victoria and Prince Albert along the High Street on their wedding day in 1840, the inauguration of the Fountain in 1877, the opening of the Swimming Baths in 1896, of the Fire Station in 1898, of Kew Bridge in 1903, of the Library in 1904 and the Unveiling of the Brentford Monument in 1909. Large numbers of townsfolk would turn out to watch processions with flags, flowers, bunting, cheering, streamers, greenery, military bands, fire engines etc, etc. Sometimes school children would be given a half holiday. Local dignitaries and invited guests would be on view. Hosts and guests would be feasted with food, drink, toasts and speeches and entertained with music, singing and dancing

To this distinguished list must be added the opening of the Great Western Dock, now known as Brentford Dock, in 1859. Being organised by a commercial company, at a Dock a little away from the town centre, it was not a public festivity in the full sense although *The Times* reports "great rejoicing". There were no formal processions and school children were not given a half holiday but it was opened in some style and memorable enough all the same

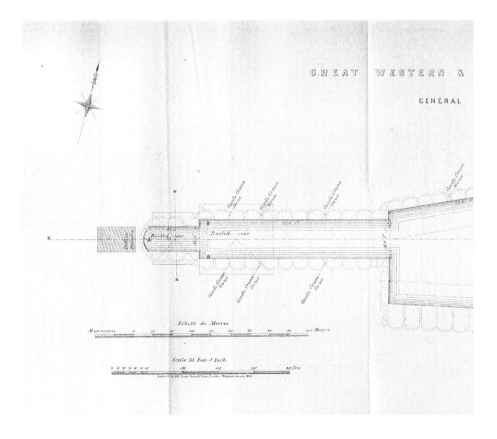

13   Plan of Brentford Dock 1864, drafted by Haskoll.
        Length of Dock from entrance to back of loading bay : 1,100 feet

The Times, Saturday 16th July 1859 : "Yesterday the ceremony of opening the company's docks and railway was performed with great rejoicing at Brentford. Special steamers from London and Westminster bridges, decorated with flags and conveying the friends of the undertaking, opened the new docks at about 20 minutes to 4. About the same time special trains started from the Southall station of the Great Western Railway to Brentford conveying the directors and their friends. The event was celebrated at the Town-hall Brentford [now the Magistrates' Court] by an excellent dinner, at which Mr. Davey, the deputy chairman [of the GW&BR Co] presided. Various loyal and other toasts were given and responded to, and the whole of the proceedings were conducted in a satisfactory manner."

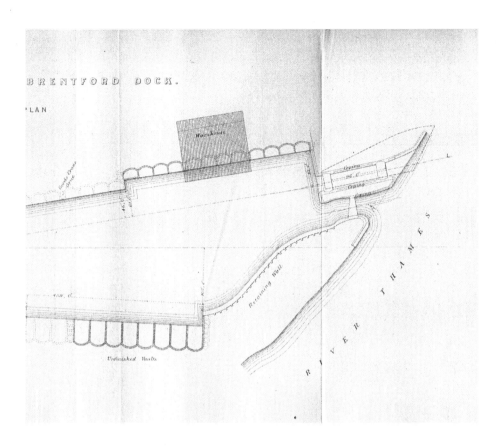

BRENTFORD DOCK.

PLAN

Shows unbuilt lock to pass single river barge north of entrance,
so plan probably drawn before Dock construction complete.

West London Observer, Saturday 23rd July 1859 : "The Directors
celebrated the opening of this short but useful line on Friday. They, with
a large number of friends, passed in the Venus steamer from London
Bridge, calling at Westminster, to the Company's Docks at Brentford,
where a very elegant cold collation was provided at the Town Hall."

In *The Railway Magazine*, R K Kirkland tells us more about the
"jollifications" (RKK,2/1960) :

The Chairman of the GW&BR Co was Viscount Villiers. As he was unwell
the Deputy Chairman Mr Peter Davey took his place as host. Also present
were Captain Bulkeley who was on the Boards of both the GW&BR and

the GWR Companies, the Earl of Shelbourne of the GWR and directors of the Midland Railway and the Eastern Counties Railway. No-one from the London & South Western Railway Co, which had opposed the Dock scheme, was invited

A select company was conveyed from London on the PS Venus and the PS Jupiter, each of which carried a band. The paddlers entered the Dock together, both bands playing "See the Conquering Hero Comes". The bands were supposed to be playing together but unfortunately there was a "slight lack of unanimity" between them. It is not recorded whether what was needed was a strong conductor or a prior discussion about keys. A special train from Southall was driven by Assistant Engineer Edward Murray. The railway passed through market gardens and the party admired not only these and the distant prospect of the County Asylum but the permanence and solidity of the railway construction

At the "repast of most recherché description" there were pointed remarks about the L&SWR Co and no toasts were drunk to them. One speaker mentioned the possibility of visitors to Kew Gardens using the new line and of "tasteful detached villas" along it. Most of the distinguished guests caught the official return train to Paddington via Southall which left rather early in the evening. Some of the less notable revellers who continued the festivities were obliged to take the aggravating L&SWR back to town

Designing, Building And Describing The Railway

Building the railway was a bigger and more expensive task than constructing the Dock. Newspaper reports hint that railway construction began at the Southall end, the most practical way to start. Once track laying had begun the railway could be used to supply construction sites from Southall. The only points of road access to the route of the track were at Windmill Lane, Brentford High Street and The Ham just outside the Dock. Road access to the Dock was always poor, even after Dock Road was complete

The Times, Saturday 16th July 1859,
with material { } from the *West London Observer,* 23 July 1859 :

"Starting from a junction with the main line at Southall, which is about a mile and a half on this side of Bull's-bridge [the London side], the new line proceeds in a south-easterly direction through a highly cultivated market garden district to the dock at Brentford, a distance of 4 1/2 miles. At present only a single line is laid, because in the first instance goods traffic alone will be conveyed upon it, but the whole length is ballasted for a double line, and platforms and stations are being constructed at the town of Brentford and at the dock for the accommodation of passengers. The formation of the line has presented few engineering difficulties; but at Windmill-bridge {a work of very remarkable character has been constructed, which exhibits at a glance Mr Brunel's unrivalled ingenuity and fertility of invention. At this spot} it was necessary to carry the railway under both the highway and the Grand Junction Canal. There are thus at this point three distinct modes of transit crossing each other, all at different angles, but having a common centre. On the top is the road, below is the canal and underneath is the railway; the total height from the rails to the road does not exceed 34 feet. To execute this work the canal had to be diverted, while a cast iron trough, 8 feet in depth was formed for the purpose of carrying the canal over the railway. The towing path consists of cast-iron roadway plates, bracketed out from the side of the trough, and the whole structure is borne upon strong abutments of brick, supported in the middle by a centre pier. 140 tons of cast-iron were used in this work, and the cost of the construction was about £5,000. At a little more than three miles from the junction the railway crosses over the loop line of the South-Western. A viaduct 240 yards in length carries it through the town of Brentford, where it crosses the London road by a wrought-iron bridge of 50 feet span {and the Grand Junction Canal by a similar bridge of 70 feet span}. From the end of the viaduct a double line is laid into the dock, just before reaching which the canal is again traversed by a bridge of 90 feet span."

Augustus Close crosses The Ham by the original railway bridge of Brunel's design. "The top flanges of the girders are curved in cross-section to give greater resistance to buckling - now such girder bridges are scarce. Extra web-stiffeners have been added and the cross-girders have been renewed, so as to disguise some of the features, but it is an important survivor." (1997,MTT)

The newspaper articles of July 1859 give technical details about the Railway and Dock. With some minor omissions, the same description appears verbatim in both papers, so the Railway Company probably issued a press release

The most spectacular operation, the double crossing at Hanwell, was apparently accomplished without problems. The route of the railway was constrained to pass between Osterley Park and the County Asylum but elsewhere it passed largely through market gardens. It may be sacrilegious to suggest such a thing but a minor change of the railway route, north or south, could possibly have been made near Hanwell, avoiding the necessity for a double crossing there. Was Brunel looking for problems to solve ? Luckily for generations of sightseers, he took the dramatic option. The first deposited plans show that the railway was not originally to pass exactly under the road/canal crossing and there was ample room to avoid it within the permitted deviations. It has been pointed out that less than half a mile away at the 'iron bridge' Brunel's GWR passed obliquely exactly over the junction of Windmill Lane/ Greenford Road with the Uxbridge Road. This junction was staggered quite early on. Fewer bridges are needed with double crossings

The newspaper articles suggest that a passenger station was being built at the Dock. Some temporary provision would have been necessary for the dignitaries from Southall on opening day, but there was no mention of a passenger station at the Dock after the opening ceremony (JEC,2000,4). There would be little need, staff were mostly local, there was no possibility of onward travel and it was not a passenger destination

Cook (BC,1994,53) suggests there was originally an engine turntable. A turntable is mentioned in the newspaper articles of July 1859, but has not

14   Bridge of Brunel's design over The Ham, looking north-east, 1958

been found on plans of the Dock. It was permissible when shunting for locomotives to work either forwards or in reverse. Locos for passenger haulage could be worked in reverse on small branch lines. A turntable was not needed, there was one at Southall and it would be an unnecessary expense at the Dock

Designing, Building And Describing The Dock

It is evident that by May 1855, when giving evidence to the Select Committee, Brunel had carefully planned the design and route of the railway and road access to the Dock from the town. But this busy man had not yet planned the Dock, he was only able to give some preliminary thoughts to the Committee. He says "I have really hardly made up my mind", "not decided", "I imagine", "I think" in some of his replies. He has in mind something like the facilities at Bull's Bridge for the Dock,

39

a few covered sidings for 8 or 10 wagons and a "slip into the river". Murray's second deposited plan for a footbridge shows the result of Brunel's turning his attention to the Dock (see Nos 6,7). It now looks worthy of the term `Dock'

The boundaries of the Dock were the River Thames, the Grand Junction Canal and a wall bounding the Duke of Northumberland's Syon Park. Its length was about 1,100 feet from the entrance to the back of the loading bay. The Dock was not close to residential areas, the high walls around some of London's Docks were deemed unnecessary. Its situation increased security and reduced the chance of complaints from local residents about night operations

A description of the Dock was published in 1870 by Isambard Brunel BCL, son of Isambard Kingdom Brunel. In Isambard's book *The Life of Isambard Kingdom Brunel, Civil Engineer* two chapters, including Chapter XIV describing Docks designed and built by I K Brunel, were contributed by William Bell. Bell, 1818-1892, who as a young man had been awarded a gold medal for mathematics, applied to join him when Brunel was working on Bristol Harbour. Bell's mathematical skills were highly valued by Brunel for whom he undertook a number of difficult engineering calculations. Isambard, who had trained as a lawyer, made use of a memoir of Bell's in his biography of his father (BDCE,2008)

Bell describes the hallmark innovations developed by Brunel in dock construction elsewhere, before using them at Brentford. Brunel used buoyant gates first at Bristol, then at docks in Plymouth and Briton Ferry before Brentford. The corrugated outline and curved batter in dock walls first appear at Plymouth, Monkwearmouth and Briton Ferry

Bell says Brentford Dock had an area of about 3.5 acres. The walls were founded in the London clay which underlay a bed of gravel of some thickness; from this there was a considerable influx of water. "The chief peculiarity of the dock is the form of construction adopted for the sides." He says that the sides of the Dock were of brick and one of Brunel's innovations was to build with brick piers perpendicular to the walls. This

15   Shipping Shed, Brentford Dock, looking westward

was for strength combined with economy in brickwork. The "piers 10 feet long and 2 ft 3 ins thick, are placed at intervals of 26 feet. The backs of these piers are connected by horizontal arches, carried up with a curved batter [leaning slightly back into the side of the Dock and curved in plan]. The piers are about 20 feet high and the arches are turned upon them, which support the front part of the quay, and meet the horizontal arches at the backs of the piers. Thus the sides of the dock consist of a series of vaults, arched over the top, and also at the back towards the pressure of the earth.

"The thickness of the horizontal arches which form the bulk of the wall is only 3 feet, but these are so strengthened by the piers in front, that a wall strong enough to resist the pressure of the earth behind it was obtained by means of a very small quantity of brickwork. Along one side of the dock [the south side] the piers are 31 feet long, in order that coal barges may lie with part of their length in the vaults between the piers while their cargo is being put on board. By this arrangement the barges have their longest

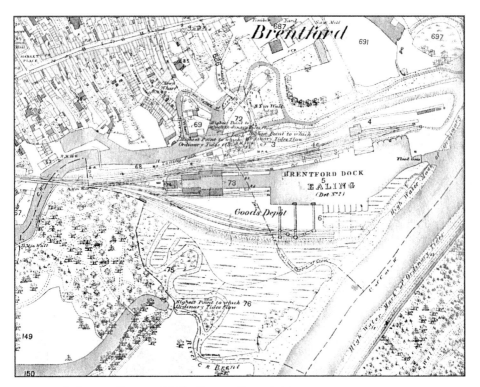

16   Ordnance Survey 1865, Crown Copyright.
Canal sidings and Syon Park sidings not yet built

dimension at right angles to the side of the dock, and a much greater number can be accommodated than if each occupied a space alongside the quay wall. The contents of the coal trucks are tipped into the barges through sloping shoots." (WB,IB,1870,441)

At Brentford Brunel's characteristic wavy outlines, vaults and vertical and horizontal arches are best seen under Marcus Court, from the pontoons in front of Numa Court, between the sites of Warehouses Nos 4 and 5 and behind Nero Court. According to the plan of 1864 (see No 13) vaults were to extend around almost the entire Dock, except for the `retaining wall' on the south side between the Dock and the Thames. Most of the vaults are dotted so probably all covered. Large vaults on the south side are labelled unfinished. Arches for the westernmost ones can be seen in the background of illustration No 39 and are still behind Nero Court

42

with the arches bricked up. They don't show on Ordnance Survey maps. The OS map of 1865 (see No 16) shows piers between the easternmost large vaults, but in the OS map of 1897 (see No 20) these piers have been removed. The smaller vaults on the north side of the Dock were covered and carried wharves and cranes with rail tracks behind the vaults

Bell says : "The entrance has a clear width of 30 feet, and is closed by a single wrought-iron buoyant gate which ... is, when shut, not quite at right angles to the entrance. The gate is 33 feet long, 19 feet high, 2 feet 6 inches wide at the middle, curved to 1 foot 6 inches at the sides, and weighs sixteen and a half tons. It is divided into compartments by four decks and vertical bulkheads. The air-chamber occupies the whole space below one of the decks, 7 feet 6 inches above the bottom; and there are two sluices, each having an opening of 4 feet by 2 feet. This gate ... has no wheel under it, the weight being carried upon the pivot. In order to

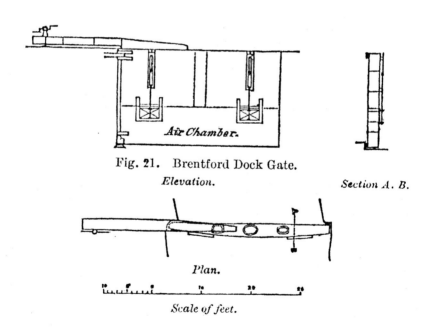

Fig. 21. Brentford Dock Gate.
Elevation.   *Section A. B.*

Plan.

Scale of feet.

17   Dock gate from Isambard Brunel's
       Life of Isambard Kingdom Brunel, 1870, p 441

43

avoid side strains upon the pivot and top collar, a counterbalance arm is fastened on the top of the gate. This is formed of two cast-iron girders, bolted together and enclosing weights between them. The ends of these girders project beyond the heel-post over the quay, as in canal lock gates, and carry the machinery by which the gate is turned ... a cast-iron circular rack is fixed on the top of the masonry, in which a pinion works, turned by gearing fixed to the end of the counterbalance. This gate turns with remarkable freedom, and the current of water running into the dock on a spring tide opens it completely." (WB,IB,1870,442). The pinion was permanently engaged with the rack

The entrance was controlled by a dockgateman. After more than 100 years, at the right state of the rising tide, the floodgate would still be gently nudged open by the water. According to Bell this was Brunel's plan. Given the designer and the design, it is hardly surprising that the mechanism worked smoothly for so long

The 1864 plan (see No 13) shows eight cranes around the Dock, four of them in the shipping shed. The cranes used hydraulic power. Francis says that, in the early 1960s, most of the hydraulic cranes were inside the shipping shed. The engine house for the steam engines raising hydraulic pressure was located on the Canal side of the site, just upstream of Thames Locks, next to the lockkeeper's premises (see No 18). The engines provided power to raise weights in the accumulator tower next to the engine house. This pressurised water which was piped to the hydraulic cranes and capstans. An example of such a system is on view at Tower Bridge

The hydraulic cranes in the shipping shed at the Dock were dated 1853, and these dates correspond with the ones from Bull's Bridge at Hayes (MTT). Hydraulic equipment installed from 1853 to 1856 at the GWR Depot, (see No 8), was transferred to Brentford in 1859. Bull's Bridge GWR Depot had been superseded by the Great Western Dock. The hydraulic machinery removed consisted of cranes, capstans, steam engine(s), boilers and accumulator. During its brief period at Bull's Bridge friction arose between the GWR and GJC Companies over the

18   Engine house near Thames Locks with roof of Shipping Shed behind. Accumulator Tower and Shunters' cabin just beyond, 1962

steam plant. The Railway Company was taking water for it from the Canal without permission. The GJC Co proposed to charge the GWR Co £20 per annum for this facility (TS). At Brentford the engine house was again built next to the Canal

West London Observer, 23rd July 1859 : "The dock itself is an important work ... . It covers 4 1/2 acres of water, having a depth of 13 or 14 feet at high water, and an ample depth to float barges at low water. There is every convenience such as covered sheds, cranes, shoots, tilts, turntables, traversing-frames ... provided in abundance, so that the shipment of goods may take place with the utmost rapidity ... it is calculated that the journey from the dock to the Pool will be accomplished in one tide. Attention has been paid to permanence and solidity in the construction of the dock. The walls, for example, have been carried down, in all instances, whatever the depth, right through the gravel to the London clay, where they are founded upon a thick bed of impervious concrete. The packing of the walls also is of concrete instead of puddle so that the dock is perfectly watertight throughout its whole area.

"Altogether it occupies thirteen acres of land, which is so reticulate with rails for the goods' accommodation that upwards of two miles of line are laid on this spot. There are space and appliances here to admit of traffic to the extent of 500,000 tons annually - an amount which the dock has been specially designed to accommodate. A telegraph from the dock to the Pool of London completes the arrangements of this undertaking."

The Dock was built as in the second deposited plan (see No 7). There are signs of economies, and it is likely that there were financial constraints. Not all the projected vaults were finished, nor a barge lock north of the entrance. As the floodgate was normally kept open when the tide was right, a barge lock would probably not have proved very

19   Lighters in the Shipping Shed. After rebuilding in steel, Brunel's wooden Shed having been destroyed by fire in 1920

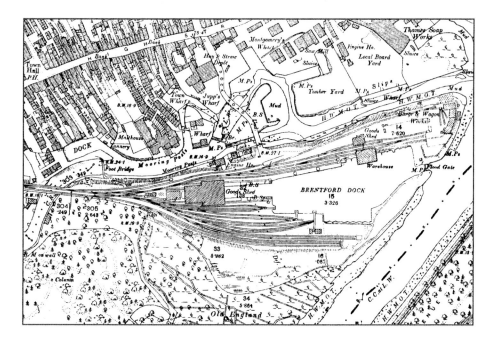

20 Ordnance Survey 1897. Shows rail tracks to coal shoots.
Crown Copyright

useful. Apparently no passenger station or turntable was constructed and certainly no footbridge across the Thames. Brunel may not have visited Brentford after construction started and he was in no position to do so as the undertaking neared completion

Further articles from *The Times*

1 September 1860 : It was reported at the Directors' meeting that progress was very satisfactory. 29 extra stations had been opened on the GWR system and the Brentford Dock line started carrying passengers on 1 May 1860. The GW&BR Co was spending money "improving and extending" the Dock and a dividend of 5% was described as being "carried forward"

23 February 1865 : There had been a falling off of import traffic but the trend over the years was a gradual increase. It was reported for the first time that the GWR Company was interested in buying the GW&BR outright, instead of leasing it

Over the next few years fluctuations in goods and coal traffic were reported at Directors' meetings but the general trend was always said to be upward. Coal from South Wales continued to be the most important commodity. It was carried almost as cheaply as by sea but far more reliably. In 1870 the sale of the railway and Dock to the GWR was recommended

Kirkland says that in the early years there was a certain amount of financial disagreement between the two companies. He says that this was not unusual between the GWR Co and small companies with branch lines worked by the GWR. It reached a point where the GW&BR Co obtained authority to inspect the books of the GWR Co to check just how much traffic was being handled at the Dock (RKK,1960,79)

March 1872 : Arrangements were finally started for a merger of the GW&BR Company with the GWR Company. The GW&BR Co said they wanted to shed the expense of separate staff, the GWR Co certainly wanted ownership of a lucrative link with the Thames

13 January 1874 : the GWR was about to lay extra rails to provide mixed gauge running for narrow [standard] and broad gauge working over the whole of the western sections of their system. Platforms and sidings would have to be lengthened [narrower trains must be longer]. Uniformity of gauge nationally would be a great boon to the public and would benefit coal merchants; coal deteriorates with handling

The broad gauge track was apparently a problem on the Dock line from the start and one track had already been made mixed gauge by 1861. It became wholly standard from 1876. The Great Western Railway was not entirely standard gauge until 1891

Coal Shoots, Cranes and Warehouses

Brunel had told the Parliamentary Select Committee that he did not suppose that there would be warehouses at the Dock (see above) but they became one of its most conspicuous features

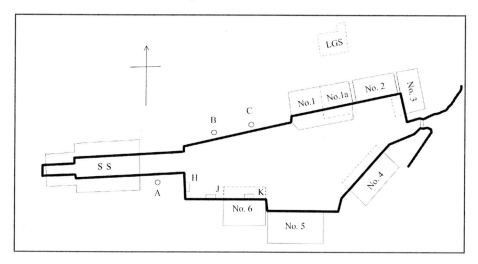

21   Brentford Dock, sketch (not to scale) showing locations of warehouses, numbered 1 to 6; cranes A, B and C; coal shoots H, J and K.

In 1992 detailed notes of dates, uses and descriptions of warehouses, cranes and coal shoots were made by Malcolm Tucker using BR archived material :

SS : Shipping Shed, 1 storey, open sides, arched quay walls, built in
        1859 originally in wood, rebuilt in 1920 in steel after a fire.
        6 cranes dated 1853, brought from Bull's Bridge GWR Depot in
        1859. Housed the loading bay with a rail siding at each side.
        (see Nos 1,13,15,16,19,20,23,31,36,37)

LGS : Local goods shed, shown on 2nd deposited plan (see Nos 7,20).
        Closed November 1930, replaced by new Goods Depot on
        railway beyond Brentford Town station in 1930

Warehouse No 1 : 1a originally built 1859 shown on Brunell/Haskoll plan (see No 13). Extended 1910s, 3 storeys, travelling cranes dated 1916 and 1917. (see Nos 1,13,16,20,24,31,32,33,37)

Warehouse No 2 : About 1901, cranes dated 1902 rest on vaults of quay wall, 3 storeys plus undercroft. Used for grain. (see Nos 1,24,37)

Warehouse No 3 : 1908, cranes dated 1902, 4 storeys, steel canopy cantilevered over dock above ground floor. Used for Lysaght tinplate and galvanised sheeting from Newport and Bristol (see Nos 1,22,24,31,37)

Warehouse No 4 : 3 storeys with neo-Georgian riverside elevation, about 1927, cranes dated 1928. (see Nos 1,24,31,32,33,37,38)

'Temporary warehouse', (see Nos 20,22,23)
    Replaced about 1938 by
Warehouse No 5 : 4 storeys, cranes 1938 and 1939. (see Nos 1,37,38)

Coal shoots at H, J and K; J and K demolished 1927 (TS); (see Nos 20,22) ,
    Replaced 1927/8 by
Warehouse No 6 : the Export Traffic Shed, 3 bays.
    Later called the Morris Shed and used for exporting Morris cars
    from Cowley, Oxford in the 1950s. (see Nos 1,36,37)

South-west of warehouse no 4 is a single storey brick building of 1938, with cranes dated 1939 (see No 29)

Reinforced concrete warehouses were an early feature of the Dock, in particular No 2 designed 1899-1901 and No 3 designed 1906-1908 (MTT,1992). Warehouse No 2 was probably the second concrete goods shed or warehouse in any British railway yard, it was used for grain. The first was at Plymouth Docks (*GWR Magazine*, Nov 1907, p 243)

In 1902 a wharfside crane rated at 2 tons was installed at A on the south side of the Dock. On the north side at B and C, a 6 ton crane and the Armstrong Whitworth crane rated at 40 tons were installed in 1905. According to Chubb, (who engagingly refers to Brentford as 'the capital

22   Coal shoot at J. After 1908, before 1927.
        Loading coal from railway truck into dumb barge to be sent to Brentford
        Gas Works. There was no rail connection between the Dock and Gas Works.
        Retaining wall and Warehouse No 3 with canopy faintly in background.

of Middlesex'), in 1922 the 6 ton crane was counted at 69 lifts in an
hour (AGC,1922,232). Cranes and hoists were installed in warehouses
in 1905, 1908, 1914, 1930 and 1937

At the riverside : According to an undated document (c1960), prepared by
British Railways (BR) for a visit by a railway preservation society, a 900
foot quayside on the riverfront was added in 1918 [as a war measure]. It
could be used by sea-going cargo vessels up to 300 tons at all states of the
tide. They were only limited by their ability to negotiate Hammersmith
Bridge. There were no charges for the use of these facilities [either inside
the Dock or on the riverfront - London docking dues were heavy] but the
Port of London Authority (PLA) levied a toll of 1.25d (a penny farthing)
per ton on freight passing above Kew Bridge. There was a uniformed
official to record traffic. Customs facilities were available to deal with

cargoes that had not been cleared at the London Docks and a Customs Officer attended frequently. The weighbridge for railway trucks (near the shipping shed) could weigh up to 30 tons

Chubb notes that the riverside wharf was served by 6 ton travelling steam cranes in 1922, but they would probably soon be replaced by mobile hydraulic or electric ones. Illustration No 24 shows two rail-mounted steam cranes carefully posed in front of the newly built Warehouse No 4 so taken about 1927/8

Later photos show two traversing cranes at the riverside straddling the railway lines and running with one leg near the wharf edge and the other side on a raised rail well above truck height close to Warehouse No 4. Records show that the high-level rail was attached to the Warehouse; the aerial photo, (see No 1), shows supports continuing alongside the Warehouse. These cranes were electric, the power being supplied via the upper track. Such 'semi-portal' cranes were necessary here to avoid two rail links to the wharfside railway tracks from the Syon Park sidings. These came in from the north side, some distance apart

23   Old England by Fred Turner, 1911. Showing temporary Warehouse, Shipping Shed, vaults, 6 and 40 ton cranes

24   Dock entrance about 1928, showing rail-mounted steam cranes,
      warehouse No 3, new warehouse No 4 and gatemen's cabin.
      Warehouses Nos 1 and 2 in background

The BR document of c1960 mentions two large electric traverser cranes
at the riverside. They were installed some time from 1928

The hydraulically-powered 40 ton crane of 1905 was originally installed
to deal with railway carriage bodies and bogeys for export. As it was no
longer in use (c1960), the maximum lifting power then available was said
to be 3 tons as follows :

Shipping shed	2 tons	hydraulic
Warehouse hoists	1 ton	hydraulic
Morris shed 15 cwt-1.5 tons and	3 tons	electric
Travelling hoists (warehouses)	1 ton	electric
Riverfront	3 tons	electric

The power house was using time-expired locomotive boilers to raise steam for the hydraulic power. Total storage space was 12,000 square yards

Chubb notes that the Dock could accommodate 1,000 wagons. Cook says that the entire site covered 15 acres with 3,194 feet of quay and 118,000 square feet of warehousing. According to a `contemporary' register there was one hand-operated tip, eleven hydraulic hoists, thirteen hydraulic cranes up to 40 tons and seven electric cranes

Working the Railway

The railway has been well covered by articles in *The Railway Magazine,* the *British Railways Illustrated Annual* and many other books and journals. The following is largely after R K Kirkland (RKK,2/1960) and B Cook (BC,1994), but see also bibliography

The Track

An early scheme had been to continue the railway across the River to Kew Gardens but this foundered on stiff opposition from the L&SWR Co. A standard gauge track was brought into use on the up line in 1861 (towards Southall) which could operate as an independent single line. This increased the area from which through goods traffic could be drawn, it was no longer restricted to the broad gauge GWR. Traffic volume naturally increased. From 1883 the track was crossed on a bridge by the then District Railway, now part of the Piccadilly line. A stop called Trumpers Halt at Trumpers Crossing was opened in 1904, to capture passengers for Wyke Green Golf course and Osterley Park. The Trumpers of Warren Farm, who had raised difficulties about the temporary canal diversion at Three Bridges, were thus commemorated. The Halt was initially spelt `Halte' to mark the fact that steam passenger railcars had first operated in France. Steam was later replaced by diesel for railcars

25   Trumpers Halt(e), before 1926. Tank locomotive

Few "tasteful detached villas" were built along the line. Development in the vicinity tended as much to the industrial as to the residential and the line served a number of factories. A short spur was built southward into the Danish Otto Monsted Margarine Works which started in Southall in the 1890s. These Works were also served by an arm of the Canal. A spur eastward went to the Associated Equipment Company (AEC) factory, (later Associated Commercial Vehicles then British Leyland) at Windmill Lane. The GWR diesel railcars built and maintained by AEC were tested on the Brentford Dock line. The Great West Road opened in 1925 and was soon lined with stylish architect-designed factories. Spurs from the Dock line went westward to serve McFarlane Lang's United Biscuits and the Firestone Tyre & Rubber Co from near the Goods Yard

Brentford Town Goods Yard was opened in 1930 for local goods, just south of the Piccadilly line and well away from Brentford town. Its main commodity was coal. As an economy measure the Dock Line was singled in December 1955. One track was lifted from Southall to the Firestone signal box, just north of the Great West Road. South of the signal box the track remained double

The Goods

In the nineteen twenties coal and coke traffic increased, minerals stayed about the same while general goods tended to fluctuate unpredictably. Goods traffic started to decline in the thirties. On weekdays there were 4 general goods and 2 coal trains down and 6 goods up. On Sundays, 1 goods, 1 coal and one mixed from Swindon worked down, and 2 goods up. Goods trains sometimes travelled empty. Traditionally trains went 'up' to London, 'down' to the country

In 1947 there were 6 goods trains each weekday with the possibility of an extra down working in the early evening if required. The speed limit on the line was 30 mph, 10 mph through Brentford station, and there were load restrictions. For instance double headed goods trains could take up to 60 wagons as long as a 20 ton brake van was attached

After the last War, four steam shunting engines were sent every day from Southall to the Goods Yard and Dock. Altogether they worked about 36 hours per day Monday to Saturday and 10 hours on Sundays. Engine no 1 arrived at the Dock at 4.55 am, engine no 4 returned to Southall at 2.30 am the following morning. Later two diesel shunters that worked the sidings were sent down the line on Mondays at 5.10 am, one to the Goods Yard and one to the Dock. They were stabled overnight in No 1 Warehouse and returned to Southall at the end of the week (SCJ,8/1982). The steam shunters were stabled at Southall and returned there each night; it was a more time-consuming and specialised job to prepare a steam loco than a diesel, they needed more frequent attention

The coal trade dwindled with decreasing use of coal after the first Clean Air Act of 1956, although general goods continued. The journey between Southall and the Dock was scheduled to take 18 minutes - could it take 18 minutes to travel 4.5 miles ? Some of these were heavy trains but this is half the speed limit. In 1962 there were still 5 up and 4 down workings each day

The Passengers

The 'Town' of Brentford Town station was dropped early on. The L&SWR station in Boston Manor Road was misleadingly named 'Brentford Central' until 1950. A passenger service between Southall and Brentford started in May 1860 with a dozen or so trains each way daily at a twopenny fare. There was never a through service beyond Southall. A Brentford Director complained to the GWR about poor passenger accommodation at Brentford, particularly the lack of a hand-rail on the steps up from the road, to the peril of ladies in voluminous skirts in boisterous weather. There was a serious lack of information, of clocks, timetables and directions to platforms at Southall

Brentford passenger trains were erratically timed, rarely with useful connections. In 1866 a letter in reply to complaints to the GWR says "we do not carry anything like half a dozen persons per train" and perhaps we can see why it was not popular. The GWR Co seemed to do little about complaints, though a handrail was added to the wooden steps down to the road at Brentford

26   Brentford Station on right. London Road looking west, 1902

27   Brentford Station on left. London Road looking east, 1935

Passenger traffic improved after the introduction of steam railcars in 1904, running half hourly at first but gradually dwindling. Rail cars had an engine incorporated and, not needing a loco, caused some astonishment. They could, if required, haul another coach. In 1910 there were 35 services each way on weekdays, 'one class only', starting at 5.45 am from Southall and 6.00 am from Brentford. The last trains were 10.50 pm from Southall and 11.00 pm from Brentford. There were 28 passenger services each way on Sundays.

Standard time for all trips was 9 minutes, passenger trains evidently worked up to the speed limit. In 1913 over 40,000 passengers were carried. Services were withdrawn in 1915 as a wartime economy measure and reinstated in 1920 with 22 journeys a day but dwindled again to a weekday peak hour service

In 1922 there were 23 passenger services each way on weekdays, and additional services on Saturdays. 14 trains worked each way on Sunday afternoons and evenings. Only workmen's trains ran from Feb 1927. Trumpers Halt closed in 1926 and was dismantled. Tickets sold numbered 33,575 in 1923, 53,000+ in 1929 and 49,883 in 1933. 1925, 1928 and 1929 were among the best passenger years financially.

In the thirties many came by train from Southall to Brentford station to shop in the town and one of the Saturday trains was said to be known as the `Pawnshop Special'. The pawnshop was Rattenbury's at 288 Brentford High Street. For many years the platform on the west side at Brentford was the only one in use. Passenger trains from Southall crossed to the up line shortly before the station. The station was neglected and became increasingly derelict

28   Thames & General lighter at Brentford BWB Depot, 1974.
Transfer between lorry and lighter

29   From Thames towing path. Showing Thames lighters, building at
      SW end of site and semi portal crane straddling riverside rail track

From the outbreak of War in 1939 the passenger service was further
reduced. In 1940 there were 14 passenger services in each direction on
weekdays morning and evening, 10 Saturday services in the morning
and at lunchtime and no Sunday service. All passenger services were
withdrawn from 4 May 1942. Brentford station was demolished in
1957

Working the Dock

Steam and, later, diesel tugs had the task of towing strings of Thames
lighters between the Pool of London and Brentford. The Thames Steam
Tug & Lighterage Co had been set up mainly to serve the Dock and were
lighterage agents for it. They had premises along Smith Hill, Brentford,
with boat yards and sheds on the adjacent Lot's Ait. These are still there

at the time of writing. Their offices were on Brentford High Street at number 41. The Company, later known as Thames & General, eventually closed in 1980

One tug would tow many lighters, depending on their loading and the conditions. Thames lighters or dumb barges do not have engines, they can only be pulled or manoeuvred manually using ropes, barge-poles, etc. They have flat bottoms and can rest safely on the river bed at low tide. A train of lighters would aim to arrive at the Dock just before high tide. A rope would be thrown from the leading lighter to a dock worker. The lighter would cast loose from the powered vessel and the whole string would be pulled manually into the Dock, with the aid of poles, bollards and the hydraulic capstans. The lighters could remain connected and go straight in as the dockgate was normally left open for 2 hours either side of high water. The operation was reversed when the lighters were ready to return to the Pool on the falling tide. The powered boat would moor outside, usually overnight, and wait for its train to be ready

30   Lighters on River Thames at Lot's Ait,
        the premises of Thames & General, 1974

In 1924 the *Chiswick Times* reported a proposal for an all-water trading route for goods out of Brentford direct to Paris. Boats from Holland certainly came to the riverside wharf in the 1950s but it is not clear that there was a ever a direct link via the River Seine with Paris. There was a customs presence at Brentford Dock from the end of 1924. That year the Dock was so busy that dockers were working shifts day and night. In 1924 40 new railway carriages were shipped to Egypt

The *Brentford & Chiswick Times* of 29 Oct 1954 lists Dock workers who would suffer during a strike : lightermen, tugmen, pokers, horse drivers and others. Barge pokers were Dock workers who manoeuvred lighters using barge-poles, they were not licensed to work outside the Dock on the river. Some of the horse drivers could have been local carters taking produce arriving by train to Brentford Market

In 1956 127,766 tons of merchandise and 9,612 tons of minerals were forwarded to London from the Dock. In the same year 52,288 tons of merchandise, 6,360 tons of coal and coke and 4,600 tons of other minerals were received from London. The Town Goods Yard dealt mostly with coal but sent 5,200 tons of general merchandise to Paddington and received 2,600 tons from there by road. In about 1960 BR recorded cargoes through the Dock :

Principal Imports : Woodpulp, starch, farina [milled grain], flour, rice, steel reinforcements, steel plates & sheets, timber
Principal Exports : Chemicals, steel tubes for oil conveyance, malting barley, tinplate, coal for home consumption

In April 1964 (shortly before closure) imports were said by BR to be as above plus asphalt, cork, aluminium, dried fruit, plate glass, plastic base materials, coffee beans, grain & seed, skins & pelts, graphite

Additional exports were machinery, china clay, condensed milk, chain & cable, scrap metal, bulk coal & coke. The 'Morris Shed' (Warehouse No 6) was used for the export of Morris motorcars, sent by rail from Cowley, Oxford

31   Dock entrance and Shipping Shed.
Gas Company tugs on left from River Lighterage, motor tug *Framfield* on
right from Thames Steam Tug & Lighterage Co Ltd. Crown copyright.

In 1929 eight canal companies linking London with the Midlands, including the GJC Co, amalgamated to form the Grand Union Canal Company (GUC). In the 20th century, for the first time, thanks to the development of pneumatic tyres on tarmac, road transport for heavy loads had become a practical option. In the 1930s the GUC developed a freight Depot based on and around the 'island' at the Gauging Locks in Brentford which flourished for 40 or 50 years. It was one of two depots in outer north London, the other being at Enfield. These depots linked road and canal transport. The canal system was nationalised in 1948 and the British Waterways Board (BWB) formed in 1963. The BWB Brentford Depot became a thriving interchange between road and canal. The Gauging Lock was doubled in 1898, Thames Lock to the Thames was widened and doubled in 1960/61. This was not long before the cold winter of 1962/3 when the Canal froze and was closed for many weeks with a disastrous effect on national canal traffic

The Dock was not designed to deal with road haulage, the interchange was between rail and river only. Picture No 33 of the 40 ton crane shows the difficulty of accessing the Dock by road vehicle. There was reasonably good road access to the BWB Depot which did not close until the early 1980s. A different story might be told if a spur from the Dock line had been carried into the British Waterways Depot and better road connections made to the Dock. BR and BW could possibly have co-operated over interchange of goods between road, rail, canal and river. Both Depot and Dock might have been kept in operation a bit longer

But it is better that Brentford was not overwhelmed by a huge trans-shipment hub and container terminal. In any case this could not have happened. Depot, Dock, River, Railway, Canal, and local roads, were all far too small

The 40 ton Crane

On 29 September 1961 the local paper *(B&CT)* dramatically reported : "British Railways engineers were investigating a mysterious subsidence in Brentford Dock. It has put the north wall with three huge cranes out of action. The ground is still sinking and now a warehouse is threatened. The wharf wall cracked on Sunday [24 September 1961] causing a 50 yard section of the adjoining railway line to cave in and the dock basin to rise a foot [?]. A 40-ton crane, one of the biggest on the Metropolitan waterways, and two smaller ones, are perched on the wall in danger of being toppled into the water. Yesterday the cranes were showing signs of tilting over. But they cannot be moved in case the wall collapses completely. Barge traffic into the lock is unaffected at present - although there is a time lag as the north wharf lies idle. First signs of trouble came over three weeks ago when tiny cracks appeared in the wall. Then while the dock was being drained on Sunday to examine the wall, the wall split

Barge built by E C Jones & Son of Dock Road being lifted from the water by the 40 ton crane. Warehouses Nos 1 and 4 in background

from top to bottom. No one was hurt and no barges were damaged. One worker said 'It happened at about 9 o'clock. There was no noise' ... the subsidence is still being investigated. But it is understood the cost of repair work will be many thousands of pounds."

B&CT, 13 October, 1961 : "Crane To Be Dismantled : A 40-ton crane and two smaller ones on Brentford Dock's north wharf which fractured mysteriously three weeks ago will have to be dismantled. That is the big task facing British Railways engineers before major repairs can be carried out on the 90 yard long section of wall and the adjoining railway siding which caved in three weeks ago. A British Railways spokesman said that a detailed examination had revealed a fractured pier of the nearby warehouse and a broken hydraulic hoist."

33   40 ton crane loading barge built by E C Jones & Son of Dock Road
      on to a flat-bed lorry from Annis & Co of Hayes. Warehouses 1 and 4
      and semi portal crane in background

The 40 ton crane was installed in 1905, Courtenay Francis mentions that it
was not protected from the weather in his time. However, the deathblow in
1961 was not a collapse of the crane, but of the nearby substructure. The
crane itself, on a reinforced plinth above the vaults, remained standing. It
seems to have already gone out of use as it was not mentioned in the BR
document of about 1960

There has been much conjecture about the cause of the subsidence, the
principal suspect being scouring by water. The newspaper photograph
and report and the aerial photograph show that ground carrying two rail
tracks behind the vaults has collapsed. The piers and most of the vaults
appear intact. BR mentions the failure of a pier under a Warehouse and
of a hydraulic hoist. The nearest Warehouse is No 1 and the damaged

hydraulic hoist was probably inside. A fracture in the hydraulic system anywhere could be a source of scouring, although a loss of pressure should have been noticed. It is not clear whether the subsidence was the cause or the result of the damage in No 1

Scouring by boat propellers has been suspected, but few powered craft normally entered the Dock. Powered boats may have needed access to the crane for special loads, railway carriages or cars for instance. The Dock is scarcely tidal but, after 100 years, tidal scouring might be possible. A vault has failed at the front. If it had also failed at the back this could have allowed scouring behind the vaults from within the Dock

The aerial photo suggests the possibility of water undermining the ground behind the vaults from the west and escaping to the Dock through the failed vault. If water from the west was indeed contributory, it is most

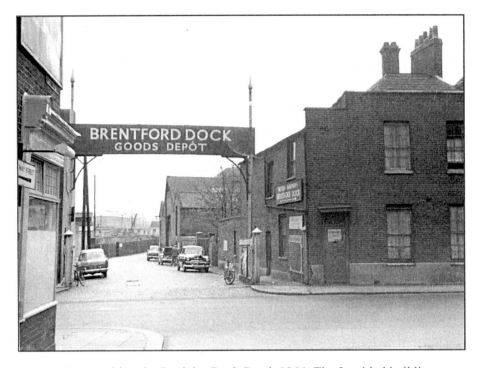

35   Approaching the Dock by Dock Road, 1964. The 3-gabled building had been Underwood's Hay & Straw Depot

likely to have been precipitation or Canal seepage. Again, leakage in the hydraulic system should have been noticed

Whether or not water scouring was the cause, from whatever source or direction, damage was extensive. Fifty yards of railway track had fallen in and part of No 1 Warehouse was involved. Illustration No 33 shows the lorry standing exactly on part of the area that subsided, which may be significant. Heavy loads would need to access the 40 ton crane from the railway track alongside

Ground movement is possible, a check for earth tremors has been made but nothing found. Sabotage seems unlikely. Apparently poor design or poor construction have not been blamed. It is difficult to avoid the suspicion that the subsidence might not have occurred had the crane not been there

68

Courtenay Francis, Recollections of a Shunter

By the early 1960s, after a hundred years of working, Brentford Dock was nearing the end of its life as a goods forwarding facility. Courtenay Francis, who worked as a Shunter at the Dock from 1960 to 1962, recalls operations at the time

Dock Road

Access to Brentford Dock for road traffic and pedestrians was by Dock Road, the only other way in was by train or boat. The bridge over the canal at Thames Locks was of wood and the first building on the right after the bridge was the clocking-in office. Further right, alongside the canal, were offices, then the engine house and accumulator tower, supplying water under pressure to the hydraulically powered cranes and capstans. The next building was the Shunters' cabin (see Nos 1 and 18). Dock and railway staff did not mix much, the Dock staff had a mess room just south of the shipping shed

Brentford Station and the Goods Yard

Trains of wagons loaded with Welsh coal came from marshalling yards at Southall and Acton for Charrington's coal depot, at Brentford Goods Yard. Wagonloads of imported scrap metal were also conveyed to Parry's scrap metal merchants, operating in the Goods Yard, later having an office at Brentford station. The shunting in the Goods Yard was done by two Dock Shunters [staff]. There was a large coal hopper and loading and unloading of coal was done by Charrington's men. Dock staff were rostered for dealing with other goods transported by road and rail. The first train of the day arrived at Brentford from Southall at about 6.00am, conveying produce such as west of England broccoli for Brentford Market Traders. This produce was off-loaded and taken by road straight to Brentford Market

69

McFarlane Lang's biscuit factory and Firestone Tyres on the Great West Road, had their own spurs from the Brentford Dock line. Empty wagons would be taken to each in the morning. Loaded wagons from Firestone's were collected at midday and brought to the Dock. When the evening train had been formed it was taken as far as Brentford and waited while the engine went to McFarlane Lang's to pick up wagons loaded with fresh biscuits. These joined the rest of the train which continued to Southall

Entering The Dock From Brentford Station

The railway entered the Dock over what is now the Augustus Close road bridge. From here sidings fanned out and wagons could be switched between tracks. Tracks led to the covered loading platforms in the shipping shed at the west end of the Dock, to the warehouses, the riverside, storage sidings and cripple sidings. Eight right-hand sidings on the Syon Park side were the storage cripple sidings where defective wagons were stabled. Next to these the main yard was used for the marshalling of trains and for stabling empty bottom-discharge coal wagons from Charrington's. The centre tracks went to the loading bay or shipping shed. The left hand sidings by the canal were the repair cripple sidings where, for safety reasons, no one was allowed without permission except the official examiner/repairer. He had a special key to clip the points. Further down on the left, beyond Dock Road, were the canal sidings

Locomotive Crews

Most trains were steam-hauled and shunting in the Dock was done by steam; locos and their crews were based at Southall. Engines were prepared at Southall and could work for 8 hours or more. Some of the trains out of the Dock loaded with goods such as scrap metal, were very heavy. Diesel engines were coming in and on cold wet mornings the gradient up to and over the Hounslow Loop could be too much for one light-weight diesel and another was needed. There was never a problem with steam

36   Entering the Dock by rail, looking east.
Shipping Shed, Warehouse 6 and Syon Park cripple sidings

Shunting Crews

The Shunters could take their breaks, brew tea and have lunch in their little cabin by the canal. Here instructions were issued by the superintendent and Shunters not currently busy could not move far away. At Brentford there were eight Shunters in all. Two at the Dock and two at Brentford Town during the day and two other pairs at night. The night shift prepared trains for the morning and were the only staff working at night. Although this meant night shunting, there were no complaints from neighbours as at Southall and Acton. At Brentford the nearest dwellings were some distance away. Night shifts were important for security reasons. [However, old people living in cottages near The Ham, between the railway and the High Street, were said to be disturbed by trains rattling to and from the Dock at night]

Working the Trucks

The central tracks to the shipping shed passed a water-column just past the canal bridge on the north side of the track, there was another water supply by the weighbridge. Here the steam locos took on water; there was no water-tower, water was delivered straight from the mains. At the west end of the shipping shed, between the tracks to the two sides of the Dock, was the wagon weighbridge with the mechanism housed in a small hut. Weighing was a great nuisance as each truck had to come back the same way to get from the weighbridge to the loading bay. It was not a straight-through system and a great deal of shunting was involved. Someone had to stand almost permanently at the catch-points to stop wagons going the wrong way and usually trucks were weighed one at a time. There was room for two normal wagons or one steel-carrying wagon, steel and cork wagons had to be weighed before and after loading

Coal in coal-trucks arriving by rail was unloaded straight into boats. Most of the wagons could be unloaded through the bottom which was done away from the crane areas, usually just outside the shipping shed on the south side. Sometimes ordinary wagons were sent which had to be unloaded by hand which was slow and unpleasant, causing complaints. The empty wagons were put in the main yard and had to be made secure by the examiner/repairer, ordinary staff were not allowed to close the bottom doors

Sidings went to two newer warehouses on the Syon Park side [Warehouses Nos 5 and 6], which held Kelloggs cornflakes

Alongside the river was a track for electric cranes [the semi-portal cranes] which unloaded steel and scrap from Dutch boats into waiting trucks. The water here was deep enough for boats to float even at low tide. Between the Dock and the river was a warehouse with a track to it on an embankment [Warehouse No 4]

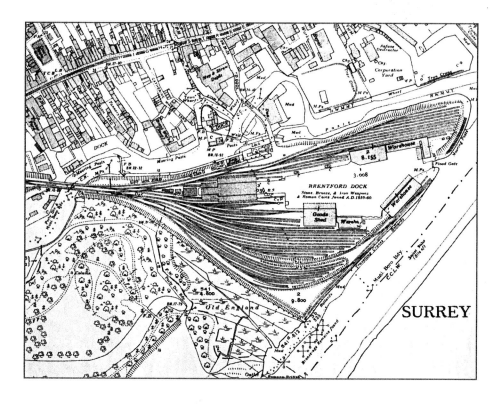

37   Ordnance Survey, 1935. Crown Copyright.

The sixteen canal sidings were used mainly for stabling wagons loaded
with sacks of starch and covered with tarpaulins. Starch was kept like this
until the customer was ready for it. The starch factory used the Dock for
storage as they had no room on their own premises and date control was
operated by the Dock superintendent. The canal warehouse [Warehouse
No 2 ?] between the canal sidings and the Dock was little used at this
time. All the warehouses had railway tracks alongside with platforms
level with the truck floors for easy loading and unloading

The Dock Entrance

At the Dock entrance there was no lock as now. A single gate called the dockgate or floodgate, was opened for a couple of hours either side of high tide and boats went freely in and out. To the north of the entrance was a hut for the gatemen who used a windlass to open and shut the gate. When traffic finally ceased the two gatemen, William Penny and William Lock, lost their jobs

38   Gatemen William Penny and William Lock (Knock)
      After a combined 93 years of service, BR did not even present them
      with a farewell gift. Warehouses 4 and 5 in background

Working The Boats

A train of dumb-barges would be towed from the London Docks by a powered barge and from the Point these trains could be watched arriving off Lots Ait. Here they divided, veering right for the Grand Union Canal and left for the Dock. A very few went further up-river to Isleworth. They arrived around high tide, as far as possible in the afternoon or evening, having spent the day moving up with the flood from London. If necessary they would moor along the river outside the Dock. A string of boats entering the Dock would cast off the tow-rope and the train would be pulled into the Dock manually. Once inside they were man-handled using ropes with the hydraulic capstans, and poles

The unloading and loading was done the following morning, but many dumb-barges were returned to London empty. The powered barge moored outside and waited for its train of boats to be ready for return to London. Loaded barges waited in the Dock where, in the past, there had sometimes been so many that men could get from one end of the Dock to the other on them. To collect the dumb-barges the tow-rope was thrown between the first one and the powered boat ready outside

The Dock

Some of the arches around the dockside were strengthened for cranes, and boats could get partly underneath some of the cranes for easier working. As built, the Dock was larger than at present, the main covered loading bay extended further westward along Justin Close. Most of the hydraulic cranes were inside the loading bay, but the big 40 ton crane was on a platform on the north side of the Dock, unprotected from the weather. The warehouses had platforms built up to wagon-floor height and side-gates of the wagons were opened. This made manual loading and unloading easier

Goods Arriving By Rail

Aladdin paraffin heaters and Kelloggs cornflakes arrived by rail for export. Much of the coal was for Brentford gas-works [which closed in 1963], some coal and other goods went on to London and for export. But by the early 1960s many wagons were arriving empty, up to a hundred at a time; trade was now mainly importing

Goods Arriving By Water

Cargoes coming into the Dock by water included rice and sugar. Timber came destined for Swindon and Spanish cork for a cork factory in Southall. This was so light that it seemed a great many underloaded wagons were needed to carry it. Boats from Holland brought concrete reinforcing bars, steel and scrap for Colnbrook Steelworks and starch for Starch Products in Slough

Their crews often spoke little or no English. The Dutch boats were the largest trading to the Dock and had to plan arrival and departure times carefully to ensure sufficient depth of water and enough headroom under London's bridges

Staff at the Dock

All the staff were men, no women were employed on the Dock. As well as the Dock gatemen and wagon examiner, staff included four superintendents, eight Shunters working shifts and up to two dozen men operating cranes and doing warehouse and barge work. Dock staff prepared barges for the London crews to collect and return them to the London Docks. Track maintenance was carried out on a daily basis by staff from Southall. At the Dock office was the Goods Agent or Manager, a Mr Vincent, later a Mr Burgess. There were four Clerks and two Chief Clerks, one called Mr Pope. The engine house was operated by two men.

Customs officials came as necessary and there was an occasional police presence for security. Each warehouse had its cats to keep down vermin and it was someone's duty to feed them. All staff were permanent and employed by British Railways Western Region, there was no daily hire system such as at the London docks. All employees were members of the National Union of Railwaymen. Pay packets were issued on Thursday afternoons

Work comes to an end

By the 1960s the busy years were over and the operation winding down. The hydraulic cranes used for loading and unloading were said to be almost 100 years old, that is, they must have been installed soon after the Dock opened in 1859 [the oldest from Bull's Bridge GWR Depot were dated 1853 (MTT)]. The 40 ton crane on the north side of the Dock suffered subsidence in the early 1960s and the management claimed that it would be too expensive to rectify it

Compiled from recollections kindly supplied by Courtenay Francis

The Dock Closes To Traffic

B&CT, 8 January, 1965 : "All was strangely quiet".

Little or nothing was made of coming containerisation as a looming problem for the Dock. Few have mentioned it. Containerisation started in the United States in the 1930s and, once the system had been standardised, spread rapidly in the US, Europe and throughout the world from about 1956. Brentford Dock had functioned effectively for over a hundred years but was too small and difficult of access by road to be adapted for containers. It must have been clear that the Dock's days were numbered. The 40 ton crane had gone out of use. After the subsidence of 1961 no effort was made to restore it and it was speedily dismantled. Brentford

Gas Works closed in 1963. Trade was falling off but the closure was laid at Dr Beeching's door. Beeching was evidently the immediate cause and, led by the press, contemporary opinion looked no further

The closure of the Dock was recorded in the *Brentford & Chiswick Times* : 24 April 1964 : Beeching's axe falls to claim its latest victim. "Brentford Dock no longer profitable". The 105-year old Brentford Dock is to close - the latest victim of Dr Beeching's economy axe. BR [British Railways] announced this week that commercial operations would cease "as soon as possible". The future of the 60-odd workers employed at the dock - which caters for goods traffic to and from the Port of London - is not yet known. Traffic through the docks has declined over the years and has now reached such a low ebb that it is no longer possible to keep open on a profitable basis. The Beeching plan has not in detail mentioned the dock ... Dr Beeching's decision has been influenced by ...
• Changes in the distribution of traffic from the Port of London
• The growth in road haulage
• Increased lighterage charges
Another factor to be taken into consideration is ... maintenance [Repairs to the north wharf after the subsidence would be costly]

The news of closure brought a hurried meeting between representatives of the three unions at the dock to discuss the future. The shut down would be a blow to barge firms, particularly the Thames & General Lighterage Co., lighterage agents for Brentford Dock. Major W L Baxendale, assistant manager of the firm, told a reporter "This is disturbing news. We have been associated with the Western Region for 80 years" [formerly largely the GWR, and for over 100 years]

1 May 1964 : Lightermen protested to Beeching that he showed no regard for workers. The President of the Lighterman's Union, Harry Watson, says that about 90 lightermen, many of whom live in Brentford and district, will be affected by the closure - it will increase congestion on the roads - there should be an integrated system where road, rail and river could

78

play their part. The Union had been told only recently that the Dock had a rosy future, but nothing had been done about the subsidence. Millions had been spent on the railways but nothing on the Dock since 1930. Mr Watson stressed the importance of the Dock during an emergency, such as the last War [the Dock had been used for the storage of ammunition]. He said that until a few years ago the warehouses were full but the rates were increased so that traders looked elsewhere

8 May 1964, Editorial : Useful parts of the present [transport] system are still being separated and destroyed. Latest victim of this lunatic policy of destruction is to be Brentford Dock

14 June 1964 : At an angry meeting organised by the River Thames Society it was said that in the 40 ton crane the Dock had had the largest and most powerful lifting crane this side of London

10 July 1964 : ... a strong hint that the 15-acre Brentford Dock site might be used for property development

1 January 1965 : British Railways confirmed last week that work at Brentford Dock was to stop today. Opponents of the closure accused British Railways of deliberately allowing it to fall into neglect; 400 lightermen would be affected. An extra 100,000 tons of freight would now go by road

8 January 1965 : All was strangely quiet since the closure last Friday

19 November 1965 : The London wharfage firm Wharf Holdings Ltd attempted to buy the Dock with a view to reopening it. But negotiations between BR and the GLC (the newly formed Greater London Council) were nearing completion

2 December 1966 : The GLC is planning to acquire Brentford Dock and develop it partially as a marine base for yachts

27 January 1967 : The London Borough of Hounslow has added its formal support to the GLC decision to earmark the Dock for residential purposes

Once claims were being made that 10% of all national trade was passing through Brentford Dock

By 1967 the way was wide open for a radically new phase

The Railway and Dock Today

Railway and Dock are now uncoupled. The Dock line was cut back to the Goods Yard in 1964 and the track south lifted. Cook notes that rail goods facilities were closed at the Goods Yard in December 1970 (BC,1994). The only firms continuing at the Yard were Parry's scrap metal dealers and Day's, who crushed stone from Westbury in Wiltshire. By 1976 there were still three trains a day from Southall on weekdays. In 1977 the GLC opened a Solid Waste Transfer Station in the old Yard (SCJ,1982). In 1982 one train per weekday brought refuse and left, bound for gravel pits in Oxfordshire carrying about 800 tons of waste

Both railway and canal are still in use, today the leisure uses of the GUC give it a higher public profile than the railway. The Dock railway is a single track from Southall to the industrial estate in the old Goods Yard. Its only leisure use is for the very occasional excursion train. This is no top tourist destination - but see below

Today the Great Western Railway Preservation Group uses premises at Southall between the Main Line and the Brentford Line. Three Bridges at Hanwell continues to attract a steady trickle of visitors to marvel at Brunel's ingenuity. The market gardens have gone and the County Asylum became St Bernards Hospital, then the St Bernard's Wing of Ealing Hospital. The work of the old Asylum is not quite forgotten, St Bernard's Wing is a Mental Health unit. From the mid 19th century

39   Dock entrance in 1971, with counterbalancing arm of
        floodgate. Shows large vaults at SW end of Dock

the Asylum was laying down a reputation as among the first hospitals
for the insane that treated patients humanely and tried to help and cure
them. The buildings still provide a handsome prospect from the west.
The built-up ground further on is landfill from waste

The old Goods Yard is well hidden. A brief glimpse of all that remains
of heavy industry in busy Brentford can be had from the Piccadilly Line
between Osterley and Boston Manor stations. Here the Day Group
crushes stone for aggregate, Pisani imports marble and granite, Stoneville
imports marble, limestone and travertine. Holloway & Sons deal in scrap
metal and Parry's is now part of European Metal Recycling. London
Concrete provides ready mixed concrete and West Waste runs the Refuse

Destructor. Lighter industries service road vehicles and offer storage facilities. The road access to the Destructor runs alongside the old railway embankment which still has half a dozen derelict coal hoppers, once discharging from railway trucks into road vehicles. The embankment is in use for storage of large plant, containers and temporary structures. Stone travels by train, local refuse arrives by road and once a day a train brings refuse from further afield

The track southward and the sidings to McFarlane Lang and Firestone have been lifted. The big girder bridge over the Great West Road of 1925, more recently a road traffic bottleneck, has gone. The Dock railway embankment can be seen on the north side of the Great West Road next to the Firestone site and from the Hounslow Loop line. The once despised

40   Brunel-designed bridge over The Ham, looking west.. 2008

L&SWR Loop thrives with four passenger trains per hour each way on weekdays, alas only one an hour on Sundays. The Dock line embankment can be seen from Commerce Road to the east and the housing estate to the west. Part of the former Brentford Town station remains at London Road, the arches still in use

In Brentford neither the road bridge nor the first Canal bridge remain. After the first Canal crossing, a few brick arches of the viaduct remain at The Ham, also in use. Augustus Close joins the route of the railway track from just south of St Lawrence's Church where a section of the embankment can be seen. The Brunel-designed bridge over The Ham has a modern precast concrete deck with tarmac and an added footway across both bridges on the downstream side. Traffic across it is restricted. The adjacent second bridge over the Canal is a replacement girder bridge on the original brick abutments. It carries cast oval plates marked "THE HORSEHAY CO LD 1932 SHROPSHIRE". Parts of Augustus Close and Justin Close follow the route of the track, curving onto the site of the loading bay on its way to what survives of the Dock

Dock Road still has its fanned sets. A metal cover in the roadway marked "GWR FIRE HYDRANT" survived until September 2008. The three-gabled Underwood's Hay & Straw Depot is on the west side of the road. Some broad gauge Barlow rail survives on the east side, in use as part of fencing. This area of South Brentford is scheduled for redevelopment. The lower part of the power house near Thames Locks is in place. It was a children's play area but now contains grass and flower beds

The Dock is much changed. The cranes, sidings and most of the warehouses have gone although some warehouse footings and ground floors remain. The ground floor of Warehouse No 5 is used for storage and as a workshop. The ground floor of Warehouse No 3 has been used for storage and the footings of Warehouse No 4 are part of a well used barbecue area. The embankment to Warehouse No 4 and most of a concrete trough marking the route of the riverside traverser cranes can still be seen. In the late 1960s and early 1970s the Dock was used as a location for films involving some spectacular controlled fires

The Dock entrance has been narrowed and replaced by a lock with a single gate at each end. The river can flow very fast in either direction and winds can be strong. There can be 'white horses' at flood tide or ebb when wind opposes current. The tide runs for 7 hours up against the stream and 5 hours down. Access to the Dock remains tricky and it has been suggested

41   The Dock gate mechanism, 2008.
In use the cogged wheel attached to the counterbalancing arm engaged with the cogged rack on the quayside

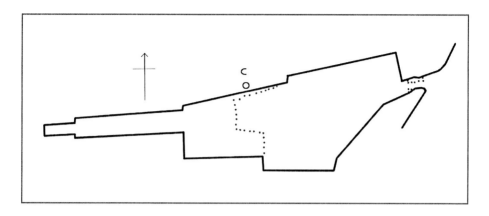

42   Brentford Dock then and now, sketch not to scale.
Entrance narrowed, western end of Dock filled in.
C marks approximate site of 40 ton crane.

that the difficulty of entering it by water is a discouragement to its present use as a marina. It has always only been possible to enter or leave the Dock for about two hours either side of high water.

The floodgate winding mechanism survives. The rack is in place but the pinion, still attached near the end of the counterbalancing arm, has been arranged on its side - as an industrial sculpture

A bigger change is that the Dock has been partly closed off and filled in. A section of the Dock wall behind Nero Court indicates its former extent. The vaults near the 1961 subsidence have been removed. There is now a low level promenade with steps down to the water in front of Numa Court. The promenade and steps turn south and continue across the Dock, cutting off its former western end and loading bay

The biggest change is, of course, the arrival of roads and housing blocks, curiously all named after Roman rulers. For more about the Romanisation of Brentford Dock see *Sir Montagu Sharpe Forgotten Man of Middlesex*, 2007, by Diana Willment

On a memorable Saturday morning in July 2001 a heavy excursion train, packed with trippers, trundled sedately down the Brentford Dock line. It consisted of two well used red diesel goods locos separated by a dozen or more veteran green coaches. A factory at Trumpers Crossing was being painted and at the tops of long ladders were two painters. They gaped in disbelief when they noticed the unlikely figment stealing by. In due course the apparition tiptoed past again, heading back towards Southall. It was a relief to find the painters still safely on their ladders, still bemused by what they seemed to be seeing

Fortunately a photographer was on hand

43   Apparition near Trumper's Crossing, 14 July 2001

Acknowledgements

Special thanks to the following to whom I am much indebted for their
sterling help and support :
    Courtenay Francis
    Carolyn Hammond
    Peter Hammond
    Malcolm Tucker
    Adam Watson

My thanks are due also to :
    British Waterways Brentford Depot
    Ealing Local History Centre
    Fuller Smith & Turner Plc
    Greater London Industrial Archaeology Society
    Hammersmith & Fulham Archive & Local History Centre
    Hounslow Heritage Guides
    House of Lords Record Office
    Institution of Civil Engineers
    Kew Bridge Steam Museum
    Local Studies, Chiswick Library
    London Metropolitan Archives
    Museum in Docklands
    National Archives
    National Monuments Record
    National Portrait Gallery
    National Waterways Museum, Ellesmere Port
    Uxbridge Library, History Collection

Keith Baker, Bob Bossine, Edward Boxell, Prof Angus Buchanan, Dr
Bob Carr, Mike Chrimes, Jonathan Crew, Ted Crouchman, Christine
Diwell, Nadine Dunn-Meynell, Alan Faulkner, Paul King, Peter King,
Pat Langley, James Marshall, Sir William McAlpine, Janet McNamara,
Dr Jonathan Oates, Bill Palmer, Prof David Perrett, Tim Smith (TS),
Peter Stokes, John Wells and many other helpful and encouraging
friends

Bibliography and Sources

1855, Record of House of Commons Select Committees

1857, 29 January, St Lawrence New Brentford Vestry Minutes

1857, *Local & Personal Acts, 20 & 21 Victoriae*, Vol I, p177

1859, 16 July and various dates, *The Times*

1859, 23 July, *West London Observer*

1864, W Davis Haskoll CE, *Railway Construction*, 2nd Series

1870, Isambard Brunel BCL, *The Life of Isambard Kingdom Brunel, Civil Engineer;* (WB,IB,1870)

1883, Minutes of Proceedings of the Institution of Civil Engineers, Vol LXXIV, Obituary, E F Murray, p 289

1922, A G Chubb, *GWR Magazine, The Great Western Railway Company's Premises at Brentford Dock*, p 232; (AGC,1922)

1927/1964, ET Macdermot & CR Clinker, *History of the Great Western Railway*

1957, L T C Rolt, *Isambard Kingdom Brunel*

1960, February, R K Kirkland, *The Railway Magazine, The Great Western & Brentford Railway*, p 75; (RKK,1960)

1976, Ed Sir A Pugsley, *The Works of Isambard Kingdom Brunel, I K Brunel, Engineer*, p 5-23

1981, *London Group*, British Waterways Board

1982, August, Stanley C Jenkins, *The Railway Magazine, Rails to Brentford Dock*, p 349; (SCJ,1982)

1982, *Victoria County History*, Vol III

1992, Malcolm T Tucker, *Brentford Dock*: Notes based on GWR Site Plan dated 23 April 1937 and other material; (MTT)

1992, Adrian Vaughan, *Isambard Kingdom Brunel Engineering Knight-Errant*

1994, B Cook, *British Railways Illustrated Annual*, No 3, Notes, *Brentford Dock and Branch*, p 53; (BC,1994)

1995, James Marshall, *The History of the Great West Road*

1999, Courtenay Francis, *Recollections of a Shunter*

2000, J E Connor, *GWR Disused Stations in Greater London;* (JEC,2000)

2000, V Mitchell & K Smith, *Branch Lines of West London*

2001, Denis Smith Ed., *Civil Engineering Heritage, London And the Thames Valley*

2002, Gillian Clegg, *Brentford Past*

2002, Angus Buchanan, *Brunel, The Life & Times of Isambard Kingdom Brunel*

2002, Diana Willment, *Brentford's Public Inscriptions*

2004, Ian J Wilson, *The Grand Union Canal, Brentford to Braunston*

2007, Diana Willment, *Sir Montagu Sharpe Forgotten Man of Middlesex*

2008, Mike Chrimes & Peter Cross-Rudkin Eds., *Biographical Dictionary of Civil Engineers*, Vol 2, 1830-1890, (BDCE,2008)

Various dates and undated :

Kelly's Trade Directories
2 documents from British Railways Board, undated (c1960) and 1964
Brentford & Chiswick Times (B&CT), various dates
Chiswick Times, various dates

Illustrations, Sources and Acknowledgements

It has not always been possible to identify or contact copyright owners. I am sorry if any copyright has been inadvertently infringed

I am grateful to the following for access to their collections and permission to use their images :

Local Studies Collection, Chiswick Library : 1,2,3,4,14,15, 16,18,19,20,22,23,24,25,26,27,28,29,30,31,35,36,37,38,39

Ealing Local History Centre : 9,11,12 from *Illustrated Guide to The Great Western Railway*, George Meason, 1852
12, Artist's impression of Three Bridges by E A L Ham

Uxbridge Library, History Collection : 8

The following have kindly given permission for specific images to be used :

Front cover, portrait of I K Brunel by John Horsley, National Portrait Gallery, London

1 and front cover, National Monuments Record, Aerofilms Collections, Copyright English Heritage

5, 6, 7, 10 London Metropolitan Archives

Institution of Civil Engineers :
13 from *Railway Construction* Series 2, W Haskoll Davis CE, 1864
17 from *The Life of Isambard Kingdom Brunel Civil Engineer*, Isambard Brunel BCL, 1870

14 John C Gillham

18 Alan Faulkner

19, 22 The Waterways Trust, The Waterways Archive, Michael Ware Collection, Ellesmere Port

21 Malcolm Tucker, for permission to adapt his Sketch Plan

30 Malcolm Tucker

32, 33, 34 Pam Vernon-Roberts (*née* Jones), photos by Gashion

40 Janet McNamara

41 and back cover, Peter Hammond

43 John Wells

Index

St Lawrence's Church 6,83
Select Committee, see Parliamentary Select Committee
Semi-portal cranes 52,53,60,66,72,83
Shipping Shed, Loading Bay 41,44,49,52,53,63,69,70-72,85
Shunters, staff 1,69,70,71,76
shunters, locomotives 56,69,70-72
Southall
1,13,15-17,20,21,24,26,27,30,31,34,36,37,38,54-59,60,69,70,76,80,86
Spurs, from Dock line 55,64,82
Steam plant, see Hydraulic system
Subsidence 64-68,77,78,85
Syon Park 3,15,40
Temporary Warehouse 50,52
Thames & General 28,59,60,61,78
Thames Steam-tug & Lighterage Company, see Thames & General
Three Bridges, Hanwell 4,21,24,27,29,30,37,38,54,80
Town Meadow, Town Mead 2,3,4,6,21,22,26,27
Treadwell (Tredwell), Thomas, Contractor 9,28,29,32
Trough, at Hanwell 21,29,37
Trumper, Messrs J & R 4,29
Trumpers Halt(e)/Crossing 54,55,59,86
Tugs 8,18,60,61,63
Underwood's Hay & Straw Depot 68,83
Unions, Trade 77-79
Vaults 41,42,43,46,50,52,65,66,67,75,81,85
Warehouses, 1,2,3,4,5,6, Morris Shed
22,31,42,49,50,52-54,56,60,64-68,70-73,74,75,77,79,83
Warehouses, concrete 50
Weighbridge, Dock 52,72
Windmill Lane 36,38,55